THE NEVER
Ending Life

A lifetime

by

Anum Abdullah

Enjoy the journey that we call life!

Best,

Anum x

**Grosvenor House
Publishing Limited**

The right of Anum Abdullah to be identified as the author of this
work has been asserted in accordance with Section 78
of the Copyright, Designs and Patents Act 1988

The book cover picture is copyright to Anum Abdullah

This book is published by
Grosvenor House Publishing Ltd
Link House
140 The Broadway, Tolworth, Surrey, KT6 7HT.
www.grosvenorhousepublishing.co.uk

This book is a work of fiction. Any resemblance to
people or events, past or present, is purely coincidental.

A CIP record for this book
is available from the British Library

ISBN 978-1-78623-116-1

Preface

Questions that are often too difficult to ask or when asked are left unanswered have been dissected in this book. Questions that often no one has the answer to due to the turmoil of emotions they cause. Emotions, struggles, daily challenges, heartbreaks, relationships; anything relating to life is what this book is about.

'Writing to the soul can do the same as what love can do to a broken heart' – Anum Abdullah.

Every chapter in this book is an exploration. There isn't much to writing; all you do is hold a pen and bleed it out on paper, whether it is pain or happiness. An exploration of what is inside a human heart or brain; the different emotions, confusions and most of all feelings that never come out. Experiences have been written about in such a pure and raw manner that it feels so real to the reader as if they were in the picture too. There are many that have been helped by the power of the words in this book and the way topics that are still seen as taboo are written about in such an honest and innocent manner.

Life isn't always great and pleasantly surprising; there are many betrayals, breakdowns and crushed souls during the journey amongst all the rainbow colours. It is like being on a rollercoaster; at times you are up and others you are down. It is like a washing machine; each wash or challenge twists, turns and spins you but at the end of the cycle, you come out brighter, wiser and cleaner of your stains.

Bleed it all out because writing my friend... is therapy.

Acknowledgements

A huge thanks to the Almighty for letting me be here despite it all, to my parents for their contribution to my capabilities to become the individual I am today and to my friends who encouraged me to do this.

Special thanks to all those people, good and bad, that entered and exited my life during the different chapters of my life, without you all this book would not have happened.

Lastly, to the one who broke me, thanks to you I can be whole again.

Introduction

The Never Ending Life is a real story about everyone's journey through life. One that is filled with rollercoasters, shocks to the system, pleasant and unpleasant surprises, the happiness of a lifetime and most importantly those silent emotions that no one can ever express due to their surroundings.

There is so much we go through in life, as an individual but there is only so much we acknowledge or let others know, even those close to us. This book discusses and enlightens the reader about the unique ways an experience or incident can be perceived, it is written eloquently in order to engage with the reader in such a way that each word has a strong lasting impact.

Life... is your very own storybook, so write as you please, but don't ever rush to finish a chapter. Enjoy each chapter and start the next one with an open mind and a fresh pair of eyes. Look forward to it. Be excited. Be brave.

And live each day like it's your last – Anum Abdullah

CHAPTER 1: YOU

Miss Independent – she got her own thing – that's why you love her.

She really was... as the name suggests and as Neyo's song goes... Miss Independent... she got her own thing... that's why you love her.

She really had her own thing; she did what she wanted without worrying about what people would think. She saw too many lives being destroyed by always worrying about what people would think or what society would say about your actions. Her belief was that it is between her and God and if she feels God won't be angry with her – then forget people. Each decision you make as an individual not only affects your entire life but also defines you as a person – some decisions show you just how strong you are whereas some teach you how to be strong. But if you've never made a mistake – it only means you've never tried anything new. That was her motto.

Being independent doesn't just mean doing everything yourself – it means not depending on anyone for anything nor needing anyone. It means being happy alone – with only yourself and your company. Miss Independent is a girl who was very shy and reserved as a child and in fact for most of her life – an introvert you could call her. Someone who was very homely and her parents were her life – she depended on her dad for everything. However, it is only those that we don't expect to let us down that do.

Her life changed the day she decided to open up – accept confidence and speak up. This girl travelled thousands of miles

1

away from home to a completely foreign country where they didn't speak a word of English for an adventure – to do something she had never done before; from getting on an airplane alone to teaching English to 30 teenagers when she was someone who was very afraid of public speaking and had never ever imagined herself as a teacher. In fact she had crossed off being a teacher as an occupation every time she was in a classroom at school.

Miss Independent – after this adventure not only completed her internship teaching English successfully while making lots of new friends as well as lifelong memories, but then went on to another new adventure – again alone – as Miss Independent. She was in China – a country that took her 15 hours to get to and so she wasn't going back home without having climbed the Great Wall of China. Despite her mum asking her not to go to such a big city alone – she was determined to climb the Great Wall of China and hence, she headed out all alone to the capital. And you must be wondering what happened next.

She left her hotel the day after she arrived in Beijing to go to the Great Wall, but not a lot of people spoke English and it was very difficult for her to communicate. It was not a place that was easily reachable via public transport and so it had to be done through a tour company. She met this strange behaving man at a travel shop – she was told she would have to take the bus to the Great Wall. However, to get to the bus this man took her in a van all by herself and with only him to the bus station. All this was very peculiar – she was sure he tried to steal her watch from her but she was wise enough to not take it off. Finally on getting onto the bus was another scary shock – no one on the bus spoke English and to top it off, it was filled with other Chinese people and she was the only foreigner. Feeling quite scared and uncomfortable she got on the bus and got to the Great Wall – climbed it and achieved her aim of visiting Beijing.

Miss Independent – she really was just that. And this is where it all began. Her journey of not only independence but of finding herself and also being herself.

She was ununderstandable... then again not everyone is meant to understand

No one in this world is the same and that is what makes everyone unique in their own way. So was she... in fact different from them all... hence, no one and I repeat no one, was able to understand her. Her ways, her thinking, the things she did, her happiness let alone her sadness.

A selfless, generous, extra-loving, independent, extremely confident and fearless young woman. That's what she was. They say we all need someone in life... but she was different. She didn't... she didn't need anyone that didn't need her... there are very few people in this world that are confident in their own skin and can enjoy their own company.

She's the girl that'll go on an exotic beach vacation... all by herself... just to take a break from her busy life whether it be work or studies. She'll go far and beyond for her friends even when she knows that some of them wouldn't return the favour. She'll find time to volunteer at a kid's school in the middle of the final year of her degree along with managing two part time jobs. She's an all-rounder – managing all her relationships – whether personal or professional is not an art everyone has been able to master... but she did or so she says, "she tried".

That's another thing about her – whatever she did or has achieved in her very short life, she never acknowledges. There is not a drop of arrogance in her. According to her not even a drop of confidence – but to some she may come across as the most confident, independent and fearless young woman ever – little do they know the storms that go on in her life, or the dilemmas she faces each day, the battles she has to fight between her heart and mind.

No one has been able to understand her – there were many who tried. Some who claimed to love her, some who wanted to acquire her and some that just wanted to get to know her. But none of them could understand her selfless nature, her

3

genuinely helpful personality or the unstoppable giggles she would break into while trying to cheer you up!

Her love was just like her – which many didn't understand. One even went as far as calling her love 'stupidity' only because his love was conditional for her whereas hers was unconditional. If she loved you, you were the luckiest person on this earth because no one, I repeat no one would ever love you more than she did. She loved fearlessly, truly and deeply with a passion that would not only amaze you but would complete you.

There's a reason why no one understood – there were many things she did which no one understood. Volunteering, donating money and time to those that needed it despite not having much herself, loving someone unconditionally despite knowing they're a cold stone and didn't know the first thing about love, or doing something for a blood relation while putting her own life on hold. At least it taught her that blood isn't as pure as it seems.

She's different – because she doesn't care that no one understands. It's funny because she doesn't expect anyone to. She's become so comfortable in her own skin that she doesn't need anyone anymore. Maybe because deep down she knows that God understands and that's all she cares about... nothing else.

Always remember: Not everyone is meant to understand you.

A little secret about Miss Independent

She's known as Miss Independent... someone who is very self-sufficient, distinct and complete on her own. She appears not to need anyone... like literally anyone. She's been on solo travels, she moved half way across the world alone, not once, not twice but three times to three very different far away parts of the world.

But who would have thought that shy, quiet and the most unconfident girl in the world would one day become someone who is filled with confidence, courage and the belief that in this world that we live in; at some point or another you're always 'riding solo'.

A little girl who lived a very sheltered and protected life until her late teens, and shocked everyone by coming out of her shell, but then again it is life experiences that shape us into who we become as an individual. She was very dependent on her loved ones all her life until that one person who she never even dreamt of being let down by, let her down in a way where they broke her completely, shattering not only her faith and trust but also her belief in relationships.

The girl who couldn't talk to her own cousins at home, because she wasn't confident enough or perhaps felt intimidated by them or just by people. It is the same girl who went onto doing presentations in front of a crowd, selling products to strangers, approaching new customers, giving talks in front of over 500 students and parents at a university. It really is amazing how life works, how people change and most of all how much we grow and change as individuals over time. Some people change for the better just the way she did, whereas some change for the worst.

Just because you have been through a tough time does not mean you have to turn into a cold, heartless insensitive monster. But everyone is different, right? Some people change for the better where they become more mature, sensible and know who to waste their time with or not. Whereas, there are some unfortunate ones too who completely break down, close their heart so tight that no one can enter.

People envy her... for her independence, her confidence, the way she carries herself and the fact that she is happy with herself, alone. She believes if you can't be happy with yourself, there is no way you will ever be able to be happy with anyone else.

It's very easy to get jealous of someone who from the outside appears to have it all figured, seems to have their life sorted and has a beautiful face decorated with a smile to die for – but you don't know the real her – you don't know what she's been through to get to where she is. You have no idea what her newly found confidence has cost her... or rather just how much she's lost to gain this confidence and independence many yearn for.

She never did jealousy and hence, never understood it. She always believed God made us different for a reason; he gave everyone a different USP, a different personality and a different story. That's all.

Truly Madly Guilty

Guilt they say can eat you up and prohibit your living. Being truthful doesn't always work out for you and appearing mad can take you places no one ever wants to see.

She was all three, so what did life now have in store for her? The bubbly girl next door who was always full of life and could bring a smile or even a giggle to even the grumpiest of people could be seen as truly, madly, guilty.

She was the truest of people you would ever meet; she'd state things the way they were, there were no little white lies with her. It was obvious she had been raised the proper way, the way most people were in the olden days before we got all this advanced technology and this dangerous thing called 'social media'. The funny thing also was that apart from her tongue being an image of honesty, so was her face. She wasn't very good at hiding her emotions or her anger, or her disappointment from her face. At times she wouldn't express it in words in situations that she knew would end up in her words being wasted, but her emotions reflected it all on that beautiful innocent face.

She was known as an absolute mad woman. She was the kind of girl who could brighten up the place as soon as she walked in, but was also the same girl who would liven up any situation with her giggles. And mind you these giggles were not only unstoppable but also dangerously contagious. She's had a laugh with the cleaner or security guard at her workplace but also giggled with the COO of the company. She's mad because she treats people with respect regardless of their surname or their bank balance. Now that for some is madness.

Guilty – the brightest of faces too have skeletons in their closets you know. She's guilty of many things, but never any that were intentional. She's guilty of falling insanely, truly and unconditionally in love with the wrong guy who didn't value her. She's guilty of going beyond the extra mile at work and being insulted and taunted for it. She's guilty of breaking the hearts of those men who wanted her for what she looked like and not what she was. But did you know most of all she's guilty of just being herself? Being this crazy, honest and purest form of a human being there could be. And if that's a crime then yes she's guilty.

Lonely – true rebels always walk alone

The loneliest moment in someone's life is when he or she are watching their whole world fall apart, and all they can do is stare blankly.

What do you do when you feel alone? All alone in this whole world, or worse when you feel lonely amongst your so-called loved ones, family, closest friends – those that are meant to love you and support you no matter what.

There comes a time in our lives when all we feel is loneliness – and it's much worse when it's with someone, rather than when we're alone. And that is the worst of it all.

You might be thinking how can someone feel alone when they're surrounded by people but trust me you can – it's worse when you feel lonely amongst people... it's the worst feeling in the whole world because at least when you are all by yourself; you are literally alone, but feeling alone while being in the company of people is a feeling you can't explain even to those you are with.

I've felt alone in a party that was thrown for me, at a family gathering, at my own graduation and worst of all at home amongst family. At times those around you can make you feel so irrelevant and almost invisible and that kills; knowing those closest to you in the whole wide world are making you feel almost like you don't matter anymore. As life has gone on, I've learnt that if your absence hasn't mattered to someone or people; neither will your presence.

The eternal quest of the individual is to shatter his/her loneliness.

You may find me weird, but I might be the only one you may hear saying that I am more than comfortable with my loneliness – yes everyone needs someone but I don't say I do. I would like someone to be there for me, that's not something I would say I NEED. There is a huge difference between needing and wanting something/someone. Don't get the two confused.

As Akon very wisely said 'Riding solo' – yep that's me! There's a reason they call me miss independent. I've learnt to be alone and most importantly be happy alone.

Learn not to depend on anyone and I mean anyone – not even blood, your parents or so called best friends – you come in this world alone and you depart alone, no point depending on anyone or making them your life only for them to either let you down to the point where you're broken into pieces or simply just walk out of your life without giving a reason. There are two possibilities that exist in this life – Either we are alone in this universe or we are not – Both are equally terrifying.

Now she just exists...

There was once a ray of sunshine. A girl who could brighten up any room that she would walk into. There wasn't a single person who didn't think of her as a breath of fresh air who could give a new life to a place or person that would come across her. She literally was Little Miss Sunshine and on some days Little Miss Giggles.

No matter what was on going in her own life, she never let it reflect on her face when she was with people; whether it be at work, with friends or with family. Having been through so much pain and misfortune in her life at a very young age, she knew how to hide her pain and not display it on her face; though unknowingly her eyes said it all despite her being quite unaware of this presentation.

Often her colleagues would ask her the reason behind her glow and her energy in the mornings at work; the question used to amaze her because she felt like the total opposite inside; be it the storm she was going through, the battle between her heart and mind or the fact that she had not had much sleep the night before.

Despite the fact that she was barely alive, all she did was help others feel good about their life and feel better about situations that they were finding tough to deal with. No matter what was going on in her personal life she never stopped sympathizing with others; she was the kind of person who would drop everything to be there for her friends whether near or far.

Regardless of the melancholy that she had been dealing with she was doing fine, going on with life and trying to get back on track. She wasn't the type of person to give up or lose hope; yes, she had been through hell and back at a very young age, but still had faith for a better future and at least a little bit of happiness.

But YOU... you broke her, destroyed her. Living a melancholic life is one thing but having been promised a lifetime of happiness by the one who is meant to be your everything, someone who is meant to love you and respect you can kill you alive. And that is exactly what you did. You killed someone who was just about alive, someone who had seen death dangerously closely; someone who was trying her hardest to stay alive and come back to life. How could you?

Remember when you met her and couldn't stop smiling, because all she did was make you happy and help you think positively? She made you feel better about your past and a lot more hopeful about the future. She has this merry and joyful energy about her which is what made you fall for her in the first place... so what happened?

How could you break someone who was already broken? How could you make false promises to a person who never expected anything from you anyway? How could you destroy someone who had just escaped a near-death experience and was just about dealing with living her life again? Did your conscientiousness not give you a jolt? Did your soul not shake when making a commitment you very well knew you wouldn't be able to keep?

Like how can you destroy a person who was there for you and supported you when you needed it the most? When your own loved ones weren't there for you?

The worse thing is that you seem oblivious to your heartless actions that ruined a beautiful heart and soul of a person who wanted nothing but the best for you, who wanted to give you nothing but happiness and a good life.

That ray of sunshine that could brighten up any room with her presence and her gorgeous smile has forgotten how to smile thanks to you, the girl who was known as a chatterbox as well as being famous for her endless giggles, has lost her smile let alone giggles anymore. She lost her charm when you betrayed her trust and broke her heart. She doesn't trust anyone anymore thanks to you, because it had taken a lot for her to trust you after everything she had been through but you took that away from her. And now... now she just exists.

Be happy with YOU

It's true that it feels nice to have someone there who loves you, supports you and will be there at every step of the way of this journey called life. However, the bitter truth is that that is not always the case. It is important to realize earlier rather than later that you come into this life alone, and will leave alone.

Be happy with yourself – that is the first step towards a happy and content life. How do you expect to make someone happy; like your parents, a partner, husband/wife, or your children for that matter, if you yourself aren't happy within your yourself.

I find it weird when people pity me for being the only child or say how weird it must be to travel alone – and I pity them way more than they pity me because they can't actually function alone – they have no idea how amazing it feels to be able to feel happy in your own skin and to be able to live alone and not feel like you need someone there constantly.

I know people, in fact close friends who can't even go to the supermarket below their apartment alone because they are just so used to having someone around them 24/7 to do everything with. And I find that so ridiculous because if you can't go to the supermarket that is literately a five-minute walk from your apartment, how will you ever live in this big wide world alone?

I've travelled alone, to countries where I don't speak the local language, where I've not known anyone – where I don't know if I will survive a whole day let alone a whole year and touch wood I have, because *I AM* comfortable and more than happy in my own company – and I believe it's not something I've chose for myself but more what life has taught me simply because of the shit that I have gone through – whether it's been being let down by those I had on a pedestal or being betrayed by friends who meant more than blood.

Life is the best teacher of all; it tests you and makes you learn the truth about how to survive in this world and on this journey called life. Yes we say life is too short – but the truth is this life is very long and you need to make wise choices and decisions in order to be able to have a pleasant journey. So let go of those that cause nothing but drama and pain in your life – cherish those that add value to your life, especially those that make you smile even in the darkest of times.

But most of all stop finding your happiness in external things and people; as harsh as it sounds, this includes parents, siblings, family and your closest friends. You've been put in this life alone and will die alone – whoever or whatever else you get or meet on the way; just treat it as a bonus because some people don't even get that. Don't ever sacrifice your happiness for those who won't appreciate it and moreover won't give a damn about your peace and happiness.

Be YOU! Be Happy! Be Content within yourself!

Find happiness in little things...

Never stop doing little things for others, because sometimes those little things occupy the biggest part of their heart. Often people forget that that's what life is about – the little things in life.

Those people are the best who treasure and appreciate a card with a few words written with love way more than costly and branded presents. Life's not about being materialistic, it's about treasuring those small things, those little gestures and heart-warming actions that make you feel alive, make you feel loved and appreciated. Often we think that in order to make someone happy we have to do something big, there has to be some kind of huge gesture and a very expensive present. But that's not always true.

For example, take most women, men think it takes a lot to make them happy but all a woman really wants from her man is respect, love and security. They'd much rather have a single rose than a whole set of diamonds. They'd much rather their man spends quality time with them than spend money on them, on things that are unnecessary just for the sake of showing off.

For example, a child only wants their parents time and love, their care and emotional support rather than for them to throw money at them. Yes it feels much better to cry in a Mercedes rather than on a bicycle, but the truth is money CANNOT buy happiness and it never does. Those with money look all nice and shiny from the outside but the truth is from the inside they are the emptiest people on this earth. They might have the most expensive things in their life but they've not tasted happiness in a very long time, so much that they've forgotten what it actually feels like to be happy.

The moment we stop expecting other people to make us happy is when we truly find happiness – when we start finding happiness in the little things in life and accepting them is when we truly find that inner peace that then leads to the happiness of a lifetime.

Happiness often comes from noticing and enjoying the little things in life...

Are You Okay?

Don't fake being okay. You'll only hurt yourself. Be real with what you're going through, just don't let it consume you. Keep a balance.

'Are you okay?' are the three words that can make a person feel emotions at the rate of 100 miles per hour. These are the only three words in the world that have the immense power of making a person realize that they aren't actually okay.

But you know what, sometimes it's okay not to be okay. It's okay to break down and cry yourself to sleep. After all we are all imperfect human beings. We are not in any way expected to be okay at all times. That is the reason why we go through good and bad times in life – so that there is a balance. Because believe it or not, the truth is if life was all good and happy and a bed of roses it would be pretty damn boring and in the same way, if it was depressing and sad at all times it would get a bit repetitive.

It's funny how humans ask each other; 'are you okay?' when they damn well know that the other person isn't okay. For example, if you're unwell, have lost someone, have had a car crash, been injured or had a near death experience. But then what do you say? What do you say to someone who is unwell with a sickness that might never be cured or end until his or her life does? What do you say to someone who has lost the love of their life or the very purpose of their life? What do you say to someone who has lost their child because of a drunk driver? What do you say to the independent butterfly who has just had a car crash and had a narrow escape from death? What do you say?

At times it's not what we say that matters but what we don't say that does. It's more important to tell someone just how much you love them and cherish them and not express how you feel. It's more important to give someone a listening ear and a shoulder to cry on rather than unnecessary advice when all they want is someone they can talk to. It's more important to send your loved one flowers just to make them smile rather than thinking about the costs associated with bringing a smile to their face. I always believe that those that are alive deserve flowers more than those that are buried six feet under.

Rather than asking those three words and reminding that person that they aren't okay – just give them a big hug and a genuine smile and tell them that 'everything will be okay' because if it isn't okay, it isn't the end. Life doesn't end after an accident, a loss, a broken relationship or the end of a life – the beauty of life is that; it goes on, no matter what, life goes on.

And with life, we must go on too. Yes, incidents happen in life which almost bring us to the verge of breaking and make us feel like there is nothing more to live for, but that's not true because if it were, we wouldn't still be alive.

A lot happens in life after which we wonder why we're still alive but the reason for that is that we all have a purpose in life and until we have served that purpose we must carry on – no matter what twists, turns and tests life puts us through – we must come out the other side, stronger and wiser.

Things are going to be okay, maybe not today and maybe not tomorrow, but eventually it will all be okay.

A Smile

For me, I never feel quite fully dressed without a smile

And I always believe that a smile is the only curve that can put everything straight. That's all it takes... a smile; to melt a heart, to show kindness, to make someone's day and more importantly to show someone you care. We don't realize this but every time we smile at someone, it is an action of love, a gift to that person, a beautiful thing.

So smile – did you know it takes more muscles to frown than it does to smile? A smile also shows us just how strong a person is, I love those who smile in times of trouble, who can find strength in distress and grow brave by reflection. It is the business of small minds to shrink, but those with firm hearts and whose conscience approves their conduct, will pursue their principles unto death.

Smile when you can – it doesn't cost anything but can make someone so rich.

Admire those that smile around you and try their hardest to make you smile even in their times of despair – those are the people to always hold onto.

Some people wear their smile better than a woman can wear diamonds around her neck, their faces are always decorated with a beautiful smile which is very endearing but can also be rather deceitful; they won't let you know if they're hurting and neither will you ever be able to find out because they love smiling.

And then there are those grumpy old sods who may have everything in the world at their feet, but there is nothing in the world that will make them smile and it is exactly them who make life difficult for other people because they think that just because they are unhappy, so everyone else has to be, but that is not how life works.

Keep away from people like that, who won't smile themselves but will not let you smile either. In life there are many times when people, either loved ones or strangers, will bring you down and you won't be able to stop them; but what you can do and what is actually in your power is to not let them get to you or lose your charm and especially your smile because of their negativity.

So smile, giggle and laugh, because life is too short to be anything else.

Written by a certain little miss giggles.

My past is my armour

Past – My past is what I have been through, it's not who I am today. What it is though is something that has helped mould me, but it does not define me. Everyone has a past and if they say they don't it's not true; it's just that they've not told you about it.

Talking about your past is brave and takes a lot of courage, especially if it's been bad and involves you having been in a dark place. And the truth is most of us have had our fair share of good and bad experiences in our past, but what is even more important is what we make of those experiences.

The memories of good and happy experiences no doubt bring a smile to our faces, on the other hand; the dark and at times life changing experiences do exactly that, change our lives but not only that, they also change us, in some cases for the better and in rare ones for the worst.

Terrible life experiences can break and almost destroy a person leading them to the wrong path in life, this isn't difficult because such incidents when they occur in life can make you lose faith in everything, whether that's in yourself, religion, family or even everything that you ever believed in.

However, truth is as clichéd as it sounds, everything in life happens for a reason. Every incident or experience we have been through has helped to shape us into who we are today and everyone we meet has a purpose in our lives. It's almost like our life is a movie and every person in our life is a character; there are temporary as well as permanent characters. Some play short-term roles, teach us something, bring us back to life or open doors we never saw being there in the first place; whereas others seem to have a more long-term permanent role.

Someone once said to me – everyone in your life is either a lesson or a blessing. A lesson in the sense that they come into your life to teach you something and once they have done that they leave because their purpose in your life has now been fulfilled. Whereas there are also those that are an absolute blessing because they are the positive people who make life worth living and make things just that little bit easier when shit seems to get real hard.

Ghosts of the past, as they say, will always be there in one way or another but it's all about how you deal with it – whether you let your past take over your future and most importantly your present, or do you actually let go of it and move on from it after learning from those mistakes.

As I always say there is an opportunity cost, not only in business, but also in every life decision that you make, whatever you choose, the other next best option will always pass you by. Life is all about making the best of what is in front of you and doing the best you can to approach every situation with a positive mindset.

Running away from your past, as I learnt the hard way, isn't the right way to go about it, you could run away from a person, a place or even home because that reminds you of whatever it is you are running away from, but life doesn't work like that. Whatever it is that you are running away from will always catch up with you one way or another. So be a man, face it! Because the truth is, running away, even though it might be an option – doesn't lead to a solution.

Treasure your past because the truth is it is what has made you who you are today, inevitably we learn from our past experiences and mistakes and that is what guides us on what not to do in the future.

So don't run away from your past, no matter how hard you try to you won't get anywhere. Deal with it, accept it and move on. Don't ever let it define you!

Have you ever lost yourself?

No I don't mean getting lost in the supermarket as a kid without your parents or at an airport or at a funfair with your friends.

Life is painful and messed up. It gets complicated at the best of times, and sometimes you have no idea where to go or what to do. A lot of times people just let themselves get lost, dropping into a wide open, huge abyss. But that's why we have to keep trying. We have to push through all that hurts us, work past all our memories that are haunting us. Sometimes the things that hurt us are the things that make us the strongest.

A life without experience, in my opinion, is no life at all. And that's why I tell everyone that, even when it hurts, never stop yourself from living. When we lose ourselves, we don't only lose the person that we were before what hit us and made us go downhill, but also we lose the things that help us live life. We lose trust in people and it's worst when it's the people that are closest to us. Yes when you lose yourself you might even lose trust in your parents, your best friend and even your husband or wife. You lose the will to live and go on with life. And the worst is when you lose the ability to feel anything again; mainly happiness.

Losing yourself is the worst feeling in the world, because not only have you lost your identity but you've also lost the will to live, you've lost the normality that is present in one way or another in everyone's lives and by this I mean, you'll stay away from home as much as possible, you won't feel like meeting your friends, you won't feel like doing, or rather have the energy, to do the things that you used to love doing before everything changed; before that one person who you gave everything to left you, leaving you destroyed, before the parent you depended on the most disappointed you and let you down, before that man who claimed to love you forced himself upon you or before the girl you believed was the one cheated on you numerous times and then left you for someone else.

Would you go back to the person you were before everything changed? Before something terrible happened that left you lost? Before you lost yourself completely? For many years I wished I could go back, go back to being that innocent girl who thought life was a bed of roses, who believed her father to be her hero, her mother to be her best friend as she didn't have any siblings and the one guy she truly, deeply and unconditionally loved to be just hers.

And then it all changed, every one of those people broke her, let her down and left her shattered; broken, destroyed and alone. So alone that now she enjoys her own company a lot more than the company of others, so broken that picking up the pieces and fixing them has made her the strongest she has ever been and so brave that nothing scares her anymore... not even death.

The bitter truth of life is that after losing yourself, YOU WILL NEVER EVER COME BACK THE SAME, but what is also true is that you'll definitely survive, you will become a better and much stronger person and no matter how hard it appears you will get through it. Because I truly believe we are never put in a situation that God thinks we cannot handle and as clichéd as it sounds, I also now believe that everything happens for a reason because the way I see it if my father hadn't let me down, I wouldn't have been the strong independent young woman I am today, I wouldn't have learnt that parents too are human and are allowed to make mistakes, I wouldn't have learnt that even those closest to you have the power to break you and let you down. I wouldn't have learnt that you come into this world alone and will leave alone and it is better for you not to depend on anyone.

Loss – can turn you cold, heartless and in some cases emotionless, as I was told I had become. But the truth is only when we lose ourselves do we find ourselves again in the sense of learning. We learn so much about ourselves. When we move away from home and the ones we love, we learn not only their importance but also our own capability; the fact that we can actually survive without the ones we thought we couldn't.

We learn just how strong we are because the thing that we thought would kill us... didn't and hence, we're still here; fighting through this battle that sometimes life can be. I always say that life is sort of like a washing machine, filled with twists, turns and spins that might hurt us and transform us from what we were to what we are but we come out brighter, wiser and cleaner. Brighter in terms of our perspective towards life, wiser in the decisions we take and the choices we make and cleaner in the sense that we've let go of the past baggage that was holding us back.

Only when we're lost can we find ourselves again.

Speechless

Ever heard of a silent baby? No right.

She was just that.

Innocent, like a child. Little Miss Giggles could talk for the world.

There was never a silent peak around her.

She could spread happiness where there's been none before. Because she was just that – the opposite of melancholy.

A heart of gold that was too filled with pureness. She couldn't wish bad for anyone, even for those that had hurt her deeply.

She had never learnt how to be bad. She was unaware of the worst side of the world that we live in. She was pure. She was innocent. Just like a baby.

A bundle of joy is a phrase that we often use for a baby but could easily be used for her because she was exactly that.

She could light up the room just with her presence. Her giggles could make you wear a big smile without even knowing what she's laughing at. She was a ray of sunshine for many; colleagues, friends, family and especially strangers. There was a certain charm about her. Her charisma had the power to light up the world.

She wore a smile at all times – no matter what was going on in her own life and at times those that knew her personally were amazed at how she would always manage to hide her pain under that big smile. At times those that wear the biggest smiles are the ones hiding the deepest of pains.

And then one day... everything changed. Her smile vanished. Or rather was stolen and destroyed.

How could someone break someone like her? How could someone take away a smile that made the world go around? Ever heard a baby just go quiet all of a sudden? No... right? And even if you did it clearly meant something was wrong.

That was the exact case with her, all of a sudden; one unfortunate day she stopped giggling. That innocent chuckle of laughs disappeared. It almost felt like happiness had vanished from the world.

Now when she smiled it wasn't a genuine one. No matter how beautifully she tried to wear her smile... it just wouldn't reach her eyes and believe you me she tried. She wasn't one of those selfish people that would drown themselves in sorrow without giving a thought to those around them. But she just wasn't successful. Her chitter chatter had gone because she had no more words.

What do you say after being broken into pieces by someone you trusted? What do you say after being destroyed by someone you truly and unconditionally loved? What do you do after being ruined by someone you considered to be your whole world? What do you say?

Unexpectedness, destruction, broken pieces, melancholy... leave you speechless because what do you do when you have no words? When you know you can't fix anything? When you can't change anything? When there's nothing left.

Her destruction left her speechless.

You're on your own, be on your own!

*'Have some fire. Be unstoppable. Be a force of nature.
Be better than anyone here, and don't give a damn what
anyone thinks. There are no teams here, no buddies.
You're on your own. Be on your own.'*
– Cristina Yang

Some of us are unfortunate enough to learn the hard way that we come into this world alone and will be departing alone. That super heroes actually don't exist in the way that the devious media portrays them to us. The real super heroes exist amongst us.

For me the real superheroes are the dads that don't give up on their children no matter how hard times get, the mothers that pluck up the courage to leave their waste of space husbands no matter how much of a taboo divorce might be in their culture, to all the victims; male and female of abusive relationships that come out the other end and give new people a chance, a chance to make them happy.

The grandparents that pick up the pieces and make sure their grandchildren are looked after and treated fairly when their parents have gone off the rails. The men and women that stay loyal to their partners after they've passed away.

The real heroes are people that have made it on their own without depending on those that only let you down. The ones that are riding solo. Because the sad truth of this life is that though we're almost always surrounded by people it doesn't mean that they're there for us. It doesn't mean that these people can't still make us feel lonelier than when we actually are on our own.

Co-dependency is a major issue that many of us deal with in today's society. It is the reliance on another being in a dysfunctional relationship, due to the other having an addiction which the other person wants to support them with and some naive ones that think they can fix them. You can't fix people, yes you can support them in getting better but you can't make them do the right thing.

Many of us depend and rely on people that we believe need help and our support in order to get better. This can be an abusive partner, an alcoholic friend, a child addicted to drugs, a man drowning himself in alcohol or those that can't live without a cigarette for more than ten minutes.

Are we God? Are we doctors? Are we psychologists? Are we angels? No. We're none of those things. So why are we so naive to think that we can actually treat these people? Why do we think we can make them see sense when they've lost all ability to make sensible decisions? Why do we think we can fix them? Why?

Be your own hero before you can go around fixing others, especially, those that are at times beyond repair. You can't tell your alcoholic husband what his addiction is doing to you, to your kids and most of all to your family.

You can't reason with your addict son about how his drug addiction is giving him a slow death, which as parents you can't bear. You can't explain your anxiety and panic attacks to your abusive partner because he'll just raise his hand again and make it ten times worse.

Deal with your emotions first. Seek help first for yourself before you go around helping others. Because the truth is if you're broken inside you won't be able to fix someone else. It won't help and they'll just keep breaking you more, bit-by-bit, day-by-day, before they've completely finished you.

Have some fire – it doesn't always have to burn, in the olden days fire was the only source of light during the night-time. Be the fire that lights up the world in this era of darkness. Be unstoppable – don't let anyone steal that beautiful smile away – the one that lights up the room as soon as you enter.

Be better than anyone here – be the utmost best version of yourself that you can manage, there is no real competition in this world, there never was. The only competition you have is with yourself. Don't give a damn about what anyone thinks – people gossip and judge, that's their job because they have nothing better to do. Remember it was never between the people and you so don't live your life according to their rules and regulations. At the end of the day it's between you and your God.

She's gone...

In my defence I was only 16, a young lad enjoying his youth and what are supposed to be the best years of your life.

I won't lie, she was drop dead gorgeous to me from the minute I saw her at work. Wearing a fitted formal black dress, she looked simple yet elegant and the dress outlined her very feminine figure in the most beautiful way. She was shaped like a guitar as the song goes. Her long hair almost touching down to her elbows but what caught my attention was a strand by her nose annoying her every time she tried to move it.

Just like any guy I was eager to talk to her; she was beautiful and very attractive and so I plucked up the courage and walked up to her. There were sparks right away; she was so easy to talk to and really interesting too; straight away I knew there was something different about her; she was unique.

As days went on we talked more and got to know each other on a personal level. We would speak on the phone for hours and time spent with her would go by quicker than a tea break at work. We got along like a house on fire; we loved spending time with each other and truly enjoyed each other's company.

However, a few months later she confessed her true feelings for me and don't get me wrong, I really liked her but I wasn't where she was at the time. I was having trouble with my ex-girlfriend who I was on a break with, I had cheated on her and yes I know I probably sound like the worse man on this earth, but that's how it was.

I couldn't reciprocate her feelings because I didn't have any for her. Yes, she was the most beautiful, smart and sexy girl I had ever met and I could talk to her for hours, but I didn't love her. Looking back now I don't think I even loved the girl I was with.

But she truly did, she loved me unconditionally then and for years to come, but all I did was hurt her, ignore her and as she once said to me... break her. I didn't know how to deal with true love; the purest and best kind. The one that makes you the happiest person on this earth because I know that's what she could make me had I taken the chance. A chance on love, the real kind. Not the one I was used to. Sleeping with the girl and cheating on her after. I can't believe I did that, but hey I was a young and immature boy who wanted to enjoy different things or rather girls before life got serious and that is exactly what I did.

She waited a whole decade for my love. Ten years. Crazy isn't it. Amazes me how she could love me after everything I put her through. Feels weird admitting this but I even remember lying to her just to get out of meeting her while she waited for me for hours in town. I was a right asshole to the one and only girl who truly loved me. I remember saying to her that I don't think even my own wife would love me the way she did.

It took me ten years and a whole lot of break ups and girls breaking my heart for me to realize her feelings, her actions and most of all her love. What I'll never forget is that I hurt her so much that she even tried to take her own life; that is something that will never let me be at peace with myself... yes I was immature but nothing should force someone to take such a drastic action.

She came and went from my life a few times as her love for me always pulled her back but since the last time she left, she's never come back and I won't lie I miss her more than ever now. I've tried to message and contact through every way I possibly could but none of her contact details are valid anymore. I feel lost. There's so much I want to say. There's so much I want to apologise for. And most of all I want to request for a chance to help her, I want to fix or at least try to fix what I broke because she didn't deserve that. No one did.

There's a reason they say that sometimes it's just too late, though I don't always believe it because it's never too late to say sorry or fix a problem but maybe, just maybe it is this time because... she's gone.

She's just gone...

The Accident That Didn't Kill Me

It had been a very good day at work; time had passed by really quickly and that's all you want on a Thursday so you can leave work and the next time you come back it would be Friday.

Little did I know I wouldn't be coming back to work the next day. While driving home from work on a cold, dark and grim Thursday, my car was stationary whilst indicating that I am waiting to turn right on a dual carriageway. When out of the blue a black car going over the speed limit smashed into the back of me.

It was so sudden, so hard and so harsh that it made my small Mini Cooper take a 360 degree turn and fall all the way on the other side of the road, from where, to top it all, a large, scary and long lorry was approaching and funnily enough, one that wasn't in the mood for stopping having seen that a huge car accident had just taken place. What the driver of that lorry had in mind is beyond me. He had seen the crash in front of his eyes and rather than stopping and actually helping me, he just kept honking at me, as if ordering me to move out of the way; as if I wanted to be in the way of fast oncoming traffic.

I had just spun 360 degrees in my small car that wasn't strong enough to take such a huge bang and wasn't strong enough to survive that; a hard impact. Luckily I managed to move my car into the side road that I was waiting to turn into anyway and as soon as I was out of the lorry's way I was safe again. It's been six months, but to date I don't know how I got out of the mean lorry's way, all I know is that I did and hence, I am here today. All it took was 30 seconds for me to make that decision to get out of the busy road, to beat death and to come back to life.

Many people have said they've had a near-death experience at some point or another in their lives but you don't really understand it or believe them until you yourself have experienced it. It's hard coming back from that; having been so close to death, coming back from death's door takes a lot of guts and strength to then carry on living a normal life, but do we ever live a normal life after a life-changing experience.

I know I certainly am not. I don't live the way I used to anymore. My motto always was that life is too short to live with 'What ifs?' but now after seeing death so closely I always say the cliché phrase... 'life really is very short'.

As human beings we complain, moan and get upset over tiny things, things that are way too insignificant in regards to what actually really matters in life. For me, having seen the light that night that perhaps had come to take me to the gateway of death made me realize that I need to live each day like it's my last, appreciate the people in my life more than I do, tell the ones I love that I do and do all and only the things that make me happy; things that would make me feel like I lived a fulfilled and happy life once I'm gone.

I stopped associating myself with people that only caused me stress and drama; people that only used me for their own good but were never really there for me when I needed them and especially the things that didn't actually make me happy but more sad. I acknowledged the fact that life is way too short and valuable to spend it on making people happy for whom your existence or happiness doesn't matter at all. So why do it?

To many I may now come across as detached and arrogant but they don't know the truth. No one knows what I went through that night when my car was hit and spun in the air; when I couldn't move nor respond to the paramedic, when I didn't know whether I was ever going to see my mum again, or be able to go home again and most importantly to be able to live again. And that's okay because not everyone is meant to know, not everyone is meant to know your story and understand it. Not everyone is meant to be there in your life when things get tough.

A million things went through my mind that day; whilst I had the paramedics in my ear, all I could think about was my mum, home alone waiting for me for dinner. Her diabetes and what it would do to her seeing me in an ambulance. No matter how good a doctor one may be, seeing your own blood on an ambulance stretcher can break the strongest of people. I thought of my father who wasn't even in the country when he should have been there by my side, my best friend with whom I had so many of my days, weeks already planned ahead and most importantly my love; though he wasn't and still isn't a part of my life, I still thought of him – the thought of me just leaving without saying goodbye. I did wonder if he would ever even find out that I had died in a horrible car accident. And of all the people really close to me and an important part of my life and a contribution to who I had become as a person.

All the worries, memories and things I still I wanted to do flashing right in front of my eyes. Me helplessly just lying there on a hard board fastened with seat belts and the paramedics trying to help me. Apparently I had been through a trauma due to which I wasn't responsive at first.

Six months ago today I came back from death's door. My one-way flight to God had been cancelled at the very last minute, when I couldn't see that light anymore that was shining through the sky at me for quite a long time until the moment I felt a sharp pain as soon as the paramedic had pressed on my chest to get a response. Six months ago today everything changed, my life and most importantly me as a person. I was given another chance at life because my first one was definitely taken away.

Six months ago I was in an accident that didn't kill me.

CHAPTER 2: LOVE AND ALL

Love... is everything?

The girl believed in love before she even knew what it meant... she believed in fairy tales, frogs turning into princes, white horses and mainly happy ever after's. Watching romantic love stories was probably not the best idea as a young child growing up. Having never seen an unhappy couple, she believed every couple lived happily ever after.

As she grew up, she believed love was everything! Literally everything. She believed having someone who loves you truly, deeply and unconditionally is everything in life and that is exactly what she wanted. She hoped that one day she would get her happy ever after, her prince charming and her one true love. Believing love is everything isn't necessarily wrong; it's just not the right way to live life. Yes love is very important in a relationship but there is something far more important and key to being happy than just love – and that is... Respect.

The dictionary definition of respect is: 'a feeling of deep admiration for someone or something elicited by their abilities, qualities, or achievements'. It basically means admiring someone deeply as a result of their personality and their actions. If the love of your life doesn't respect you and most importantly treat you with respect – his love won't ever matter because without respect, love is lost.

The girl for whom love was everything in life – more than money, status and everything materialistic, fell in love and that is exactly when her bubble burst – she realized that love is not everything, as she had believed all her life. Yes love is beautiful, magical and can make the world go round but not without respect.

Two people that love each other must first respect each other in order for their love to last and grow. When she found the love of her life, she was happy at first, she had felt something magical after a very long time, but as expected it didn't last because he didn't respect her. He ridiculed her, thought she was stupid for making certain decisions, decisions that made her happy, decisions that let her be herself, selfless. He broke her confidence and then slowly and gradually broke her; he was the only person who could. He was the only person who was able to break her... he broke the girl who was full of love. Her love was so pure, so true and most surprisingly so unconditional. He broke that love and destroyed it.

Now the first and most important thing for her isn't love – it's respect. The girl who only longed for love, now only longs for respect. She is now willing to live her life with a man who respects her but may or may not love her. Because after all, love isn't everything in life.

Her love...

People often think about the one they say they love late at night or at the end of a long day but the truth is when we are all alone at night, we are only thinking of the person who removed loneliness from our life. True love is remembered and missed at 2pm in the afternoon amidst a busy and hectic day at work rather than at 4am in the morning.

And that is exactly what her love was like, whether it was her drive to work, her walk to the corner shop or while browsing in a busy shopping mall, she always thought of him, it would only take the smallest thing to remind her of him. I would say to remind her of her love for him, but the truth is that love, her true, passionate, pure and honest love for him never left her for her to be able to remember it again.

No matter what she did, it was always there at the back of her mind, her heart. Perhaps, this is one love that even surprised God. After all, how could someone so young, innocent and oblivious to the world love another human being so much to lose herself completely?

She truly loved him, as much as she knew about love.

May he be happy... my love

"I can make you happy... I thought I was changing your mind," were my last words to him.

I had been deeply hurt by those closest to my heart and even those who lived in it, but still had faith, a little glimpse of hope that one day everything would get better. That one day all the calamities that I had been put through would result in something rather positive. I knew I had come out of each of them much wiser, stronger and brighter... but that didn't mean it didn't hurt.

So why couldn't you?

You said I made you happy, I was just about the only reason for you to wake up in the morning, for you to want to live a little in the time that we did spend together; so why couldn't I make you happy enough to change your mind? Why couldn't I make you believe in me again? Believe in yourself again?

All the possibilities we had talked about? When you had requested me to drive you around in return you'd fly me around once you had your pilot's license, your request to me to make that God awful smelling Chinese, which God knows what made me agree to. Guess it was my care for you, my wanting to make you happy, so you felt like you could trust women again; guess I was just being me again.

So what changed? Did you not want Chinese anymore? Remember the first time we met; how easy it all was, the flowing conversation, the unstoppable smiles on our bright faces that glowed as a result of the spark ignited between us on our very first meeting. It felt so bizarre, never had I felt such a quick connection with anyone before. It felt comfortable the way our conversations flowed, we didn't have to think of topics to talk about because we never ran out. There was never a dull moment when we were together, rather quite the opposite where we had smiled so much together that our jaws would end up aching.

So why couldn't you stay? Was the happiness we shared not enough?

The promises you had made still echo in my ears, the beautiful picture you had painted for both of us still bright and clear in front of my eyes; throwing me off every time it flickers in front of me, making me wonder as to what changed? Where did the strong commitment disappear to all of a sudden? Why did you let go of our future so easily, without a single moment of hesitance?

So was your happiness not in line with me?

Was I just a pastime as they call it? Spending time with a woman without any strings attached is an attribute of the rich. Is that all I was to you? Someone you can create special moments with, those filled with happiness and joy; leaving painful memories post separation?

So did I mean nothing to you all that while?

How do you leave someone when you promised to be by their side through thick and thin? How do you promise a commitment despite their doubts and then break their trust anyway, just when they've started trusting you? Like how do you break a completely innocent, kind hearted and genuine person who wished nothing but well for you? How do you just leave without saying Goodbye?

Wherever you are, may you be happy my love. Hope the freedom you fought for was well worth it and has brought you peace with yourself.

May you be happy... my love.

A Woman's Love and Hate

No one has ever been able to win against a woman in love, nor have they ever been able to beat her when it comes to hatred.

Love – one of the most beautiful, purest and deepest emotions of mankind; though it may seem humans these days don't know the feeling even if it hit them in the face. They say there's nothing greater than a woman's love in this world; whether it be a mother's or two lovers.

Though called weak by body, women are the strongest species among mankind. There's a reason God has given men physical strength whereas women have been given both physical and emotional strength. For that very reason God has given a woman the privilege of being a mother; of bringing an actual human being into this world. Despite the immense and absolutely unbearable pain that comes with childbirth; a weak species as society sees women is the only source through which children are born.

Women don't need men but the other way around; first they need a woman in the form of a mother who brings them into this world, nourishes them and makes them into a young man. After which they are passed onto the next woman in their life; their lover, the one who moulds them, teaches them about adult life and is always there for them through thick and thin. It is not to say that a mother's role ends here because that never happens. A man will always need his mother.

If you've ever had a woman in your life who has been true to you, you'll know that a woman loves so passionately, deeply and most important of all, selflessly. Only a woman is strong enough to forgive her man countlessly; whether it be for love, for the sake of her children or for the sake of her man himself. She will always try her hardest to save her relationship, her marriage and most of all her love.

While on one hand, a woman will do anything to save her love, forgive her man and be there for him, on the other if you wrong a good woman who has only wanted the best for you, been there for you every single time you needed someone and forgiven you every time you messed up; she will walk away and never come back. There's a reason they say a woman's love and hate cannot be compared.

When she's had enough, she really has had enough and when that 'feelings' switch is off; there's nothing in this world that can change it. You can do the most extravagant and romantic things for her but it won't make the slightest difference. Lie after lie, betrayal, cheating, abuse, negligence; a strong woman can take everything a man throws at her but not disrespecting her soul.

The same woman that loves you, despite everything you put her through, can hate you with more intensity than the intensity with which she loved you. The one who cared about you despite going through shit herself cannot give a damn about you once she's washed her hands off of you. The same woman who was the kindest person you knew could be the coldest living corpse you'll ever come across, once you've hurt her to the point where you've killed her inside.

Never hurt a woman or any person who truly loved you or cared for you. People hurt others without realizing and when they're told about it, they deny it or pretend to be oblivious to the fact. But the harsh truth of life is that when someone states you've hurt them you don't have the right to judge whether they're right or not. You've hurt someone be the bigger person and apologise. You never know when that apology may come back and save you.

Many may not believe it, but karma is an absolute and utter bitch. It is the truest of all truths. As Justin Timberlake sang, "what goes around comes around". And boy does it come around. It might not happen right away but one day when you're not even thinking about it, it'll come around and bite you in a way you could have never imagined.

Never underestimate a woman's love. No man has ever been able to beat the love of a woman nor has he been able to compete with a woman's wrath.

Trust

To be trusted is a greater compliment than being loved.

Trusting someone is a huge risk; a gamble that we often are ready to play because the truth is you never know just how much you can trust someone.

Trust – something that is more easily broken in today's day and age than actual glass. It is mostly broken by loved ones, friends and sometimes strangers; but strangers you can expect it from, not your own.

Trust is something that once broken can never be the same again.

After all, how do you trust someone again once they've broken your trust?

How do you trust someone who's not kept your secret? Who's blurted out your personal and confidential information to someone who didn't matter?

Trust, something so difficult to build but yet also so easily broken.

But why is it broken? Why is it so difficult?

Why would you break the trust of someone who trusted you with their secrets, their personal information and most of all their whole life?

How can you do that to someone so close to you?

Why would a best friend betray you and break your trust? The same best friend who was meant to be a sister. The one you would share all your secrets with.

How could a parent betray the trust of his or her own child? The child they brought into this world themselves. How do you break the child that is so vulnerable, weak and most of all in need of your love and support?

Why would you cheat on the one you claim to love? The one you said is 'the One', the one you had dreamed of spending the rest of your life with? How do you even have the power to hurt and break them to the point where they lose themselves; to the point where you've completely destroyed their soul and broken their heart?

Trusting someone takes a lot of courage and strength; especially for those who have had their trust broken by people they never dreamed of doing so. Breaking it on the other hand; might not take a lot, but once broken is almost impossible to repair because the person whose trust you have broken, by breaking their trust you have gifted them with a life-long fear. Fear of having their trust broken again, fear of trusting someone at all again, fear of a loss of relations and most of all fear of losing everything that they lost when you broke their trust.

She wasn't unlovable...

Heartbreak after heartbreak, betrayal after betrayal and one mess after the next; can either make or break a person. How do you go on after being broken, destroyed rather and most of all let down by the one person who you never thought would hurt you? Being broken into uncountable pieces when the one person she truly loved destroyed her.

How can you love someone unconditionally, so deeply and purely that in doing so you almost lose yourself? How does someone love so selflessly that they completely forget themselves in doing so? When all you've given is love and never got anything back... it kills you. It can destroy you, not only emotionally and mentally but also physically and psychologically as well. It can make one think of them as unlovable, as worthless and most importantly as nothing. That's exactly how he made her feel. It was almost like he made a joke out of her love.

Her love for him was absorbing her all over; it was almost like she was drowning in the sea with no one there to save her; an accident just waiting to happen, despite the one that she had just about avoided whilst she was with him. There was a time they had met and as she had walked off to go home, her love left her looking back, wanting more and before she knew it she had reached the road and was just about to get hit by a bus but... God saved her; just like the numerous times after that meeting He had saved her despite the uncountable times she had tried to end her life, just because the one person she had wholeheartedly loved didn't love her back. But not only that, had made a completed fool out of her love and the most beautiful emotion itself. The one thing that makes the world go around had completed destroyed her and destroyed her life.

She started feeling insecure about herself, about her looks, about her weight and most of all about her personality. She had started thinking whether she was too fat, too dark, too bubbly, too chatty or too everything for him. She had started doubting herself, the way she was with him and everything she had done for him had suddenly been put under a microscope for her. Had she been too lovey dovey? Had she expressed her love a bit too fully? A bit too honestly? Her love that was so raw and so pure had not been understood let alone reciprocated. In fact it had been broken, ridiculed and most of all thrown back in her face.

How could a love so pure and honest not been understood? How could he not see that she loved with him every breath she took, every beat of her kind heart, every bone in her body and every tiny particle of her self-being? How could he not see how pure, kind and genuine she was? How could he not acknowledge her care? Her concern? Her kindness and most of all her empathy towards him?

He being stone-hearted and cold destroyed her. She started believing that there was something in fact wrong with her and not him. Whereas, the truth was that he was the one who was the problem. He was the one who was not worthy of true love. He was the one who did not understand the pure and true emotion that love was. He was the one for whom love meant a one night stand rather than a lifelong commitment, companion and partner.

Because of him she thought she was unlovable, which certainly wasn't true. Just because one doesn't understand your love does not mean that you are not worthy of love. When the time is right, the one who will value you and understand you will also love you. He will love you at a time where you might think you are unlovable for most, because the truth is the right person will love you, not only at your best but also at your worst.

What is love?

People often ask.

They think love is having a romantic candlelight dinner for two in a gorgeous well-lit restaurant with flowers and soft music everywhere; the man pulls out the chair for his lady, passing her roses that he has bought or even ordered for her and showing off to the world, what a gentleman he is. No, for her true love meant bringing her paracetamol and a tub of her favourite Ben & Jerry's' after she's had a bad day at work and has a headache. True love for her meant she'd buy his favourite fruit drink first thing in the morning and give it to him; only because he had said he had a craving for it the day before.

Someone who was as sensitive, innocent, pure and honest as her could only understand her love. But he wasn't. And so he didn't understand... and perhaps never could or ever will. Despite knowing and accepting this fact, her heart still doesn't let go. Her heart still believes in her God and her true love for him because she believes that God only gave her all the pain that he knew she could bare, but also believed that even if he didn't, God recognized and valued her love for him because it was that pure. No one had ever loved a man as much as she did. So honestly, generously and selflessly, because that was her; she was all those things without even knowing.

You would think how could someone who was loved so deeply not be able to see it or even feel it, but he didn't. He felt nothing... nothing at all. And that is what destroyed her. Her love for him, her care, concern and most importantly her wait; meant nothing for him. The world called him the luckiest man on earth, but just as she was oblivious to the world, he was oblivious to her love, which is what destroyed her.

The colourful butterfly who wherever she flew, left a mark in the world, by spreading colour and happiness, all of a sudden turned black. She wasn't vibrant and lively anymore, it was as if someone had stolen her charm away and left her lifeless. They say that is what love does, but she didn't believe them. Love doesn't destroy you, break you, hurt you and squeeze the life out of you... no it doesn't; people do.

Though she stopped believing in love, her heart didn't. She physically couldn't and never will be able to because of the way she is. Her soft, caring and genuine nature will never make her cold or heartless, but she started believing that she was. The way he destroyed her down to the ground and left her broken... into tiny pieces that even she couldn't put back together... but everyone believed that she would, one day; because time heals all.

You've been scared of love and what it did to you...

Our first love is someone we can never forget and if truth were told why should we?

They were the first ever person that we truly loved, adored and gave our everything to.

The first person we had those romantic and emotional feelings for.

Love, they say is a very strong word, but what some forget is that it is a rather stronger emotion, one that can make or break a person.

These days love has a rather bad reputation, as it is available rather easily but that is what people think, but isn't necessarily true. The truth is love is very difficult to find these days, rather next to impossible because of the notion of temporary love that we have. The one where sex is more readily available than food to the hungry, where it is easier to talk to a stranger than it is to talk to those closest to you, to the point where strangers are better listeners than your best friends.

Love has a terrible reputation not because it is an emotion that breaks you, but because the people who misuse it are the ones who break you. The girl who left you hanging because she wasn't fully over her ex, or the one that left you the minute you lost your job, or the one that was only with you because you had the money to maintain her fake image.

For ladies, the dickheads we have to deal with are just... I don't know where to start. The one you truly and unconditionally loved was cheating on you the whole time, the one who left you for his ex though she completely broke him, the one who strung you along but never actually wanted to be with you, the one who claimed to love you but physically abused you to the point where you lost yourself or the one that forced himself upon/raped you just because he could.

Love is one of the most beautiful emotions on this planet and not just romantic love but love in general; the love you feel towards your pet, who is just like a baby to you, the love a new mother feels before she has even set eyes on her newborn child, the love a sister feels for her younger sister and the most powerful of all; the one you feel for 'The One', your soul mate, the one you think you can't live without.

Many of us have been betrayed, cheated on and destroyed (BCD'd) in love as I like to call it but truth is, that wasn't love, because love doesn't do that. Love doesn't destroy you; rather it is the only thing in this world that keeps you going, which gives you the strength to be whole again after being broken bit by bit, it gives you the will to live again after you have lost everything that you lived for.

It may seem impossible but trust me you will love again, it'll never be the same way as you did the first time, but it will happen again with the right person and at the right time, but for that to happen you will have to give love a chance, give life another go. There's a reason for everything that happens in life, agreed we may not see it or understand it at the time but eventually we all do.

Someone once said to me, "Everyone that comes into our lives is either a blessing or a lesson".

Friendship and love...

Two very strong emotions; different but at the same time quite similar in the emotions and feelings department, where on one hand friendship means having someone who will be there for you no matter what, to see you through the dark times, to make them a little brighter when life's a little dark, to laugh at you when you fall before finally picking you up, to make you smile when you can't stop crying and to be there for you no matter what.

Love on the other hand includes all of the above and so much more, friends come and go but the true ones stay, love never leaves. I always believe that you either always loved someone or you never did because love never leaves you nor does it leave your heart. You will move on, 100% you will, but the truth is a teeny tiny part of you will always love that person. You will also love again because the myth that you only fall in love once isn't true. You fall in love many times in life with different people. You fall in love with your mother the minute you lay eyes on her, your father when you get to know him, your siblings despite them being a pain in the bum at times, your friends who become family and most of all the special man/woman in your life, which is the most special kind of love we will ever feel because they are the ones who give us the love of a child – motherhood or fatherhood.

You are one hell of a lucky person if you fall in love with your friend/best friend because there's a reason they say that you should marry your best friends. I also believe that and at least for me personally if he can't be my best friend I can't marry him because you can't marry someone without having some form of friendship with them.

Not everyone will admit it but all any one of us wants is love and no, before you think everything girly and romantic, let me stop you there. That's not what love is about. Love isn't all about sex or a romantic candlelit dinner or a bunch of roses. Love is about your other half standing by your side when things get tough, when you lose your job, when you're diagnosed with cancer, when you develop post-natal depression or when your business goes bust.

Love is about being there for the one no matter what, even when they appear unlovable, selfish or difficult. It's seeing past their flaws and still being able to cope, go on with life and be there by their side. Love doesn't just mean hearts and roses – it means so much more. Love is about companionship, having that one person who you can rely on no matter what life throws at you because let's face we all come alone and leave alone. Today we live in such a world where you can't even depend on your own, your parents, friends and in this world full of selfish people if you are lucky enough to have that one person who can be your world – you don't need anything else.

Why do you love me?

Love – the single most beautiful, unconditional and life changing emotion on this planet. An emotion that makes you blind, one that impacts your ability to see right from wrong in a negative way and also one that makes you a giver – someone that only keeps on giving without expecting anything in return.

And just exactly like that there was a girl who only knew love in life, it meant everything to her and soon it became her life – or rather he became her life. She was in love with someone who didn't know the meaning of the word, someone who never loved anyone, a person not even worthy of being called a human being due to his inhumane qualities.

He was as heartless as she was kind, he was as cold as she was warm and he was as selfish as she was selfless. Where she'd sacrifice a leg and an arm for him, he'd try and break her with every stone he could find. Where she was always there for him and always supported him, he was not once there for her or gave a damn the day she ended up in hospital.

Stupidly and naively she still believed in the power of true love... in the power of the universe helping two people come together that were meant to be. She hoped and waited, waited for him to change, waited for him to realize her love, waited for him to acknowledge all her actions that made her this amazing, selfless and wholeheartedly generous girl who only knew how to give.

Anyone would think that after receiving so much love, even a stone would grow a heart, but that never happened with him, he remained as cold and heartless as a corpse and to date still is. He was a player after all, selfish, self-centred and unworthy of love. She didn't exist for him apart from the time he needed someone to talk to. How do you expect someone whose heart was broken so deeply to believe in love anymore? And yes as expected she stopped believing in love, she didn't believe in what is known as the most beautiful and heartfelt emotion in the world. All because of one bad seed. She had waited years for him to say those three words to her... or for him to even realize just how much she loved him, like truly loved him – but he never did.

And just because of him the girl stopped believing in love. She deprived herself of finding love again. Her trauma was so huge that it prohibited her from even using the word 'love' in general conversation. She lost self-confidence in herself and in her ability to hold down a relationship. "Why doesn't he love me?" was a question that didn't let her sleep, a question that made her question her existence, her love for him which she believed to be true unconditional love.

A girl so broken from an emotion as pure as love completely lost faith in it. And ironically one day when she actually heard those three words that she had yearned to hear from the one person she truly, deeply and unconditionally loved from another – she had no words. She wasn't a liar but felt immense pain hearing those words from someone to whom she couldn't say them back to but one thing she did say was...

... *Why do you love me?*

The Spark!

*"They say the best kind of love is the kind that awakens
the soul and makes us reach for more, that plants a
fire in our hearts and brings peace to our minds"*
– Nicholas Sparks.

Two people, from very different worlds and mind-sets came together as a result of destiny in a rather odd and unexpected setting. Little did they know what destiny had planned for them... a love stronger than ever, a passion that never dies and a flame that is forever ignited. They met when they were young, immature and unaware of what life holds; the ups and downs, the good and the bad and most of all the complications that love brings in the best of relationships.

The minute they connected, there were sparks flying, their eyes wouldn't leave each other's, as clichéd as it sounds it was love at first sight. A love that they both were unaware of, a love so strong and powerful that it would win against all odds, a love that brought two complete opposite ends of the world together.

These two people were meant to be, but of course they didn't know that, despite all the flying sparks between them, which probably needed a fire extinguisher to be put out. As it usually happens, life gets in the way of two people who love each other being together.

They never officially got together but whenever in the next nine years of their lives, they met and spoke, their spark was always there. No matter how heated the situation, nor how emotional they both were – that spark always ignited, flaming, bringing them closer together every single time. Unfortunately, for them they never realized any of it, they never took into consideration the one thing that was always there between them – the spark – that never died.

Why is it that the spark never went away? Why is it that no matter how long after they spoke the spark was always there?

Every single time, they met or spoke that spark was still there. In relations such as family, friendships and old romance, the spark dies down after not speaking for a few days, months or years, but not with them. At times they went years without speaking, but not once did it have an effect on their spark. Their spark lived on and still is even if they aren't together or who knows if they ever will be.

x Some sparks never die x True love lives on forever x

Dear love...

Dear love,

As I promised to tell you everything, here it is. I miss you... more than ever... more than I could have ever imagined humanly possible to do so.

I didn't think saying 'see you soon' at the airport would turn into me waiting around for what seemed like a 'Goodbye' to end. It hurts. Not knowing where you are, how long you'll be there or whether or not you're okay absolutely kills. You know I've never been good with uncertainty. I wish there was a way to make this easier.

Crying like two little babies at the airport just showed how much we had fallen in love with each other and now here we are; miles apart with no telecommunication possibility but only these letters. It almost sounds like some chick flick romantic movie.

Watching you go that day broke me or should I say I felt like I lost a part of me. I wanted to stop you from boarding that flight, from leaving me; from leaving the country you had fallen in love with but what could I have done or said? You had to go. You knew that and I knew that. What we didn't know though was just how strong our love had become.

I wore your favourite dress to work today and as soon as the elevator doors closed at work and I saw my reflection; a sharp pain went through my chest as I realized that you weren't there by my side. I had worn it to the football match that you had got us tickets for and you had absolutely loved it on me. Little did you know it become my favourite dress since that day too.

Sitting in my room waiting for the phone to ring just so I could hear your voice is something that has become the norm now. I very well knew you had another life that I wasn't a part of and it was your work, but little did I know it would be so hard not hearing from you. Not knowing if you were okay, your whereabouts or what you were up to. But mainly whether you'd still remember me or not. And it hurt the most the moment I'd have doubts of whether or not you were missing me the way I would miss you.

Please don't forget to wear your blue shirt to work on your first day tomorrow with my favourite red tie – looks amazing on you. Tell any girls eyeing you up to come and talk to me! Hehehe. I hope you have a great day back at work. I know it'll be a long and hectic day so don't forget to have lunch on time and your usual yoghurt snack too – we all know what happens when my baby is working hungry. Try not to get grumpy on your first day – just eat well.

I wish I could be there with you. To fix your tie. To kiss you goodbye. To tease you every morning like I always used to and to make you feel like there was always a surprise waiting for you at home in the evenings.

Anyways... I gotta get going... heading to the gym... I spend a lot more time there now that I don't have to rush home to feed a hungry baby (haha) plus also because I don't know where to go. Home doesn't feel like home anymore without you. The teddy you got me is the only thing waiting for me at home and it even reminds me only of you. Not sure what to do.

I love you... stay safe... see you soon.

A Valentine's Date for a Non-Valentine Girl

It was the day before Valentine's Day a boy had travelled a few hundred miles just to be with his girlfriend and the love of his life.

His love was so that he did everything possible to spend the much celebrated day of love with the girl he had been in love with for somewhat four years after finally getting the chance to be with her; to call her his. His girlfriend. His love. Something he had always hesitated to say out loud to anyone but mostly her.

He was ecstatic to have gotten the chance to celebrate the day with her but little did he know that she wasn't someone who was a big fan of Valentine's Day – not because it was more a commercial day and that she believed that every day should be a day filled with love when you are with the person you truly love. But the reason was something else – she had nearly killed herself over her one true love a few years ago – yes it had been a while, but not for her. For her the day every day felt like the one where she arrived at death's door thanks to someone who didn't love nor appreciate her. And hence, she wasn't particularly thrilled about celebrating the day, even if it meant she was going to be with her boyfriend. However, she made every effort to make it special for him because she believed that her past, her grief and her pain shouldn't have an impact on someone who truly loves, his day shouldn't be ruined over someone who didn't give a damn whether she lived or died.

She cooked for him and they had a lovely candlelit dinner where even though the food was delicious, he couldn't take his eyes off of her. Despite her effortless appearance in casual jeans and top, she looked amazing. For him – she was the most beautiful girl ever. She had a planned a walk after dinner for them along the lake but he wasn't interested. He didn't want to see the famous lake in her city that she had been banging on about, but was more interested in just being around her, even if it meant hanging out in her apartment. All he wanted was her. Her company. To finally be able to hold her. Touch her. Kiss her. Adore her. And tell her all things that he had been bottling up and keeping it to himself for four long years.

On Valentine's Day – they did go for that walk along the lake because she wanted to show him how beautiful it was and, once they got back to the apartment he had a surprise in her room waiting for her – there was a beautifully wrapped present on her bed with a box of chocolates and a lovely card and the bed was made too.

Once she gave him his presents he was ecstatic, simply because in the short time that they had been dating, every present she got him from the bunch was something he liked whether it was a dreadful *Star Wars* pair of socks, a Mr & Mrs mug or a Darth Vader T-shirt. Everything symbolised him and things he liked. No one had ever given him a present like that. So thoughtful, taking into consideration every detail.

This was coming from a girl who ran away from Valentine's Day like the plague. She was also a girl who cared about the feelings of others more than her own; especially if it was someone she truly cared about and she did care about him; a lot.

He got up from his chair and gave her a big hug to appreciate her gestures and thoughtful efforts. She was pleased and relieved too that he had liked the presents because she had been very nervous. Hours before their Valentine's dinner table reservation they stayed in each other's arms; cuddling, kissing and whispering sweet nothings in each other ears.

So this was a successful Valentine's Day Date with a Non-Valentine girl that ended in a romantic candlelit dinner at a lavish restaurant where he ended the night buying her her favourite flowers – a bunch of beautiful roses.

Fanaa

Fanaa is an Urdu word that means to destroy or annihilate. Sufis use the word to describe the extinction of the human self in the universal being. It is often used in Urdu with the meaning of being destroyed in love.

You may think how can one be destroyed in love, but then again if you have fallen in love then that is exactly what happens. You don't fall in love for safety or for comfort. They say fall in love not with the one you can live with but with the one whom you can't live without. The one you'd be ready to destroy yourself for without having to think about it.

Love – an emotion so powerful that it holds the strength to not only change a person but also cause destruction that they are not the same person anymore and can never be.

There was once a girl who fell in love with a flirtatious and notorious man who was often reported as a player. They met while they were both on holiday; they met on a tour that they had both booked to explore the city. There was something about her, the minute he saw her all he could speak in were poetic lines. As a result of who he was, her friends warned her and so did his. But she seemed to have already fallen for him and so did he for her as it appeared.

For a flirt he was the most honest one, amongst all the flirting and the time that they both were spending together he had put it out there that he wasn't looking for love nor did he believe in the concept of it. The more time they spent together the more she fell for him and no matter how much he denied it so was he. Her smile that made him go all soft inside and go crazy with happiness. Her eyes that spoke of more purity than her heart that was made of gold. The way she used her fingers to push her hair behind her ear every time he said something that made her nervous, or rather weak at the knees. He had fallen in love. A love that he felt was making him weak – because he wasn't allowed to fall in love. By his very own rule.

The last day before their holiday ended they spent every minute of the entire day together, in each other's company and eventually in each other's arms. That evening after a dinner that he had cooked for her in his apartment, they sat together in each other's arms by the fire to keep warm. They talked about anything and everything. She told him how she had her whole life planned out from the degree she was doing, the job she wanted to the age she wanted to have a baby. She was a very organized and determined, independent young woman; which was rather funny as he was the opposite. The holiday they were both on was a perfect example as it was a very last minute decision for him to jump on the same flight as his friends – but it was the only last minute decision that he was proud of.

As they both felt their love grow for each other they ended up making love that night on the most beautiful of nights, with the moonlight reflecting in their faces and bodies engulfed in each other's fragranced loved. She was shocked; she was always someone who wanted to wait until marriage for sex but that is exactly what fanaa means. She wanted to get destroyed in his love, he made her feel emotions that she had never felt before. In the very few days they spent together they both felt happiness that they had never experienced before.

Though they exchanged contact details, she never heard from him ever again but she didn't complain. She found out that she was pregnant a few weeks later but wasn't upset about it. She didn't inform him because he hadn't replied to any of her former messages and so she accepted the fact that at least she got to experience the beautiful emotion of love in life and was now left with a beautiful memory of the one she loved in the form of a child who she named after him – Raphael.

Dear Love – Part 2

I won't say I miss you.

You only miss people that you forget.

And believe it or not I still haven't been able to forget you. How can I? How do I do it? I really wish I could. Not because I don't love you but because I can't take the pain anymore. The pain that loving you has caused me and still is continuing to do so. Loving you has broken me. Every ounce of love I have for you is giving me a slow painful death.

Why do I still love you? A question I keep asking myself every day. A question that keeps me up all night. A question that breaks me every time I feel that pain.

Love isn't always about getting what you want. It isn't about gaining love in return of loving someone unconditionally.

And it certainly isn't about forcing someone to love you. They say it's better to have loved and lost than to have never loved at all, but I think I may be the only person to disagree. Losing someone you love hurts like hell. You can't control death and I acknowledge that, but is it your fault to have been left behind? Is it your fault to not be able to forget the one who is gone? Is it your fault that with their departure it is your life that has taken a standstill? Is it your fault that you are suffering from survivors' guilt? Is it?

Loving you doesn't seem to get easier for me. Tell me what to do. Please let me go of this love. It isn't letting me live. The constant pain doesn't allow me to breathe freely.

It's truly amazing how you can still love someone who broke you with all those broken pieces. I still do. With every broken piece, I still love you.

Two negatives

They say opposites attract, when they see two people that are completely different from each other come together. And they say 'two peas in a pod', when two people who are alike come together. But what do you say when two people that have been broken to the core come together? What do you say when two negatives come together?

Can two negatives coming together make a positive?

They were both broken. She had been destroyed by her one true love; the one she had dreamt of marrying and spending her whole life with, the one she would do anything for.

And he had been betrayed and cheated by his first love, there's not much to say about her other than the fact that she was a money grabbing cow; all she ever wanted him for was his money in order to maintain her fake lifestyle.

The two had been betrayed not by love but by the two people they had loved the most in their lives according to them. The two people who were the first ever people they had trusted with their hearts. Your heart is a vital organ for your body, but not just vital for you to live but more than that vital for you to survive. Survive the cruelties of this selfish, twisted and at times disgusting world we live in.

They came together at a very strange and delicate time in their life. Both very raw with their wounds. Both hurting in a pain that wasn't letting them live peacefully.

But their meeting was perhaps, what was written in their destiny. After all only two halves can make a whole again and that is exactly what they came together to do.

She was the complete opposite of his first love; she had no interest in his money, instead all she wanted was his time and respect. She wanted to get to know him, get to know his pain even and try to help him. She knew very well the kind of pain he had been going through because the pain he had been experiencing for a mere two years, she had dealt with for a whole decade, yet she was still here.

He was the complete opposite of her first love too. He wasn't a player and respected her and all women, unlike her first love who merely saw them as a sexual object. He didn't eye her up despite how stunning she was because he had shame in his eyes and didn't see women as just humans you can use in the bedroom. He wanted a companion he can build a life with, have a future with and more than anything build an understanding and she was exactly that.

They were both nervous when they first met; but little did either of them know that they would get along like a house on fire. There were no awkward silences in their conversation; it just flowed like the waves in the ocean. Their laughter could be heard from a mile away and radiance had captured their faces with sparkle spreading in their eyes.

They were meant to be. They completed each other. In religion, it is said that a husband and wife are like garments that cover each other and complete each other. They cover each other's mistakes and fulfil each other's shortcomings as well as cherish, motivate and always encourage one another. And that is exactly what both of them were to each other.

Who says two broken people can't find love again? Who says they can't be happy again? Yes; your first love is special and nothing and no one in the world can replace that person but that is only because they aren't meant to be replaced. You weren't meant to be and neither was your love. You will love again and it won't be the same because it isn't meant to be the same. It's a different set of feelings because the first time, it was all pain so how can it feel the same way?

Two negatives came together as a result of destiny and made a positive.

Stay positive... anything is possible.

Made in Heaven

'Matches are made in heaven'

We often hear our ancestors and elders say that matches are made in heaven and that it is already written as to who we are meant to end up in with in life the moment we are born. I never used to believe it before but having seen some real life examples, I now do. It is true that we only end up with the person that we are meant to spend the rest of our lives with.

For example, a dear friend who is very beautiful, intelligent and a gem of a person got married at a rather young age to a man who was meant to be the perfect guy for her. They had a rather grand wedding, one that the whole world came to and remembered. But unfortunately it didn't last more than five years, that too because my friend tried her hardest to make it work with a man who was an alcoholic, abusive as well as jobless. It is amazing and quite shocking how he had changed so soon after marriage. It amazes me how people change colours more times than a chameleon.

And then a few years after the divorce she actually ended up with someone who had proposed to her before her first marriage as well. It amazes me how in the end she got married to him. Both of them doctors. Now it was the perfect match. He respected her, admired her strength and most of all loved her for what she was back when he first fell in love with her and even more now when he saw what or rather who she had become.

From a personal experience as well I can say that no matter how much you want to be with someone or make yourself believe that you need them and can't live without them, you will never end up with them if you are not meant to.

It's funny how life works; you can spend a decade truly loving someone and actually planning and wishing a life together but one day part ways for various reasons and never came back together. But then why did destiny allow you to spend all that time together, why did fate bring you together? A decade is a long time in which a lifetime of memories are created.

Perhaps, matches are truly made in heaven and we only ever end up with the one person with whom we are destined to spend the rest of our lives. That one person who is meant to be your happy place. That one person who becomes your everything, the one who makes you realize why it never worked with anyone else.

I thought you were my happy place...

Having been through hell and back at such a young age opens your eyes to a lot of things in life. It definitely makes you a lot wiser and unintentionally helps you mature way quicker than you should have.

It is strange; life is. Just when you give up and lose all hope that things will ever get better, something out of the ordinary happens; someone extraordinary comes into your life.

I ended up with a job at my dream company of when I was a teenager when I had lost all hope. It was unbelievable. That is exactly when I realized that I went through that rejection after rejection just because it wasn't time then. It didn't work out anywhere else that I had applied to because I was meant to be at the company where I had dreamt of working for god knows how long.

Similarly having had my heart broken by my first love, who was also the first guy ever in my life, I lost all faith in love, I lost faith in the world and emotion. The girl who was a diehard romantic and could die in love stopped believing in the world's most powerful emotion. How sad could life get? Then came you. Out of the blue. After a very long time I actually saw a pinch of light at the end of a very dark tunnel that I had been walking in for as long as I can remember.

I was nervous at first to get to know you, to get close to you and most of all to let you in... but I did. I gave you a chance, gave love another chance and most importantly gave life another chance... especially after having seen death so closely.

You made me smile, laugh even, but most of all you made me believe in second chances again. Little did I know, you were just like me... broken. We both had very similar pasts and unfortunately had had similar life experiences which is what made us click I guess.

We understood each other and our point of views matched because we knew what it felt like to be destroyed by someone we dearly and truly loved. How it felt to be let down by our loved ones; be it parents or best friends. You found me understanding and easy to get along with and I found you straightforward and honest. We made a good team. After all we did get along like a house on fire. I still don't get how two people who met for the first time after four years can get along like there have been no gaps in communication. There were no awkward silences as I had expected nor were there any pauses in our conversations... it all just flowed.

You made me happy again and I know I made you believe in love which I'm not sure how I did as I still didn't believe in it myself. I guess at times you don't know what or how much you actually are doing for someone until they actually tell you and make you feel appreciated. I honestly thought you were amazing. I admired your honesty and your attitude towards life and most of all *US*. You had started bringing me back to life without even knowing. Having had to deal with a bunch of assholes, I had stopped expecting an actual nice guy to come along and you did exactly that – proved me wrong.

You were the exact opposite of anyone I had ever met. You were honest, unafraid and most of all just yourself around me. You didn't hide anything from me from the very beginning and that is what I loved about you.

I never told you this but I thought you were my happy place... The one person, the one place where I would feel safe, feel happy and most of all feel loved. You respected me for who I am and I really admired that. You appreciated me for what I had become and for everything I did for you and that was important to me. But most of all you made me want to live again and that... that was invaluable.

CHAPTER 3: MISSING SOMEONE

I Miss You...

Some mornings still feel like the night before. I'm just waiting for the days I don't miss you anymore.

I never knew missing you would hurt so much... or that I would miss you at all. People say death is the greatest grief of all... I say no; the greatest grief in life is losing someone who is still alive but isn't in your life anymore. Whether they don't deserve to be there or have simply just decided to walk away.

Missing someone who has passed away; doesn't get easier with time but you feel better with time knowing they are in a much better place now, where they are free from pain and agony and one day you will be reunited with them.

Missing someone who is alive but not a part of your life anymore kills... pains like nothing you have experienced ever before. And that is how I feel right now. I miss you. I miss you like I've never missed anyone before. Though I miss you... I feel like I am missing a part of me almost. I love how the French don't say I miss you when they miss someone as we do in English but they say... 'Tu me manques' which translates to – 'you are missing from me'. The French are called the best lovers for a reason after all.

But yes you are missing from me. You came into my life uninvited... the way love normally does and little did I know or ever imagine that you would become a part of me. I was a complete mess... a broken shattered girl who kept running... running away from life... from her country that she called home because her pain lived there... she couldn't bear to be there anymore. I was fine though. Or at least I pretended pretty well to be. Why did you have to come along? Why did you have to get so close to me? Why did you bring down my walls that I spent so long building? I had sworn I would never fall in love again or be able to be close to someone again but YOU changed that. You taught me how to love again or shall I say to feel again. I had been told that I had turned into a girl who had gone too far away from her feelings. But YOU made me feel again! You breathed life back into me. My melancholy had turned me into a lifeless person who was just living for the sake of it.

They say everything happens for a reason... were you the reason I am alive today? Were you just sent to me so that I would come back to life? So that I would move on and forget the pain that had been eating me up inside for eight long years?

If so... why is it that I feel more broken then I ever did before? Why is it that you left me so wrecked that I don't believe anything or anyone will be able to put these pieces back together? Why is it that I don't feel like smiling anymore whereas around you I never stopped? You called me crazy while still loving my little Miss Giggles moments where I would smile and then end up in giggles while playing with you – the way you looked at me then made me feel like no one else would ever be able to look at me the same way. Why oh why my love did you do this to me? I thought you were my healing drug... little did I know you were the poison that was going to give me a slow painful uninvited death.

They say you know you're getting bad again when your mind and body just want to stay in bed... I guess I am getting bad again... waiting for the days I don't miss you anymore.

The missing piece...

It's funny how life works out... there's always a huge differ-ence in the end in what you had envisaged and what actually happened. Sometimes someone comes into your life... they make you forget all your sorrows and make you feel happiness like you've never before... but then life happens. From being the missing piece in your life... they become the piece that broke you. You were exactly that... and here I am... broken. Not sure what's going on or why. Just feel broken.

I wonder why you came into my life or why I came into yours. I knew my habit of being selfless will get me here one day. That day when you opened up to me by the stairs, or hugged me outside the supermarket or when... when you cried your heart out on my shoulders near the river... I wish I had walked away... as heartless as it sounds I really wish I had because trying to help you with your pain that was killing you inside has got me here. And I am not even sure where 'here' is.

I envied you that night for crying your heart out in front of a stranger... that's all I was to you. Whereas I can't even cry in solitude or in front of friends, let alone a complete stranger. It's funny, trying to eliminate your temporary pain has left me with a lifelong one. One that I have no clue about. All I know is that it hurts. It kills. And it doesn't seem to go away. And what breaks me even more is that you don't know my state... you think I'm happy and everything is hunky dory... well that's not how life works. You always were different. Very delusional and unrealistic about life.

I truly hope one day you realise that in eliminating your pain... you weren't successful in actually eliminating it for good... but rather you just transferred it all over to me. Then again you always were selfish. It amazes me how you can sleep at night... knowing you broke someone... someone like me. I can't say that about a lot of people in my life but I can for you... and today I will – I truly wish from the bottom of my heart that *I NEVER MET YOU.*

This time... last year

There's always a lump in my throat when I look back to this time last year... looking back makes me smile but always leaves a tear in my eye.

This time last year... I was happy... I had you.

This time last year... I was content... I had us.

We were happy, I was happy or at least I made myself believe that I was... despite all the fights, the control, the drama, the doubts, but it all didn't matter because I had you. You made my life hell with your doubts, your controlling and aggressive nature and possessive attitude but just one smile, one sweet genuine compliment and that one hug – it made everything all right. Each time it happened, it gave me back that hope that you can change, because you loved me, surely you didn't like seeing me all scared with my eyes decorated with tears all the time. Though looking back you never really cared when you made me cry.

I wish I could only remember all the pain that you caused me and forget about all the happy moments we had... it makes it all the more harder to move on... to move on from you... from our love... from our memories.

That day when I cooked for you and drew a little smiley face on the rice with the vegetables, it took me ages... yet you didn't appreciate any of that... that hurt! I only did that especially for you... you knew how much I hated cooking. That day when you shouted at me in the middle of a busy platform at the train station... why did you do that? It was Valentine's Day – a day I don't celebrate but did that year especially for you. You ruined such a beautiful evening only because of your anger. I even had a surprise planned for you later that night – it involved your favourite chocolate cake! You had no idea how little you made me feel that night amongst all those strangers at the platform just staring at me.

Every memory has a pain linked with it. But why is it that the heart only remembers the good times? The happy times, your smile and my unstoppable giggles. Why is it that I can't remember the painful times – the times that you broke me bit by bit? We were together... happy... content... so in love. It's funny how you came into my life... uninvited. Gave me so many happy memories along with so much pain to last me a lifetime. It was like we lived like a married couple... the ups, the downs and everything in between. We created a lifetime of happy memories with a pinch of bitterness in what wasn't even a year.

This time last year... I had you... it was hard... you were breaking me but truth is that you also made me happy... or maybe I was delusional. I mean how can you break the one you love but you did. This time last year... I was breaking... bit by bit by someone who loved me and someone who perhaps I loved...

This year... I am broken... but healing... only thanks to you... because if you were here you'd still be breaking me.

A year ago – today

A year ago today – exactly on this date, was the very last time I ever saw you, held you and felt your arms around me. Until now it hurts when I think about that day because I feel like I lost you forever that day. I remember telling you that I had a feeling that that day was the last time I'd ever see you.

And funnily enough or shall I say sadly enough, it was true because I never did – we had a trip planned in October which never happened. I had so many plans for you, all the presents, the flowers and the cake I was going to bake for you... and most importantly the love... our love.

Till the time we went downstairs to wait for the cab it hadn't hit me that you were leaving, someone I deeply loved and had become a part of my life; every single day of mine started and ended with you. Whether it was the good morning and good night texts or our never ending conversations about nothing and all sorts; the movie and pizza nights, cooking for each other and our weekends – those were the best ones.

So many memories of our weekends spent together, they really were the best! You leaving a year ago today meant that I lost all of that as well – all the memories, the happy and sad moments but it was still loss – one that you never understood; and how could you? You started a whole new life thousands of miles away from me; physically as well as emotionally. They say grieving the loss of someone who is still alive is worse than that of someone who is dead. And now I understand why they say that.

I've never ever cried so much in my life let alone at an airport like I did on that day – we both did – we cried our hearts out because I guess somewhere deep down we both knew that that was the end. That perhaps maybe just maybe we would never see each other again. It wasn't just you leaving me that day – it was our love as well, a love that was wrong, a love that was toxic; one that brought only pain, destruction and death. Death of our love, our emotions and most of all our relationship.

That one day changed everything... you leaving changed everything... I changed everything... dealing with your loss made me do things I would otherwise never do but I was a mess, the distance was killing me day by day without me realizing it and doing something about it and hence, we ended up like we did.

A lot has happened in the past year but what I will never forget is a year ago today – because that was the last time I saw you my love, cried while holding you tightly in my arms. Remember when we were sitting on the floor, you holding my hand and crying while I was trying to console you? I kept saying we'll still be friends but you didn't believe me nor agreed to it.

I wish I had never held that hand ever, but at times I also wish I had never let go of that hand... my love was true no matter what you think, feel or believe. Those emotions at the airport were true, those unstoppable tears that wouldn't stop for weeks even after you had left were real, so was the pain in my chest, every action of mine for you was genuine and my love was pure. I might have not said it enough but love is something that requires to be felt. And no matter how much you deny it... I know you felt mine.

I wish you'd talk to me...

Someone said to me today that communication is key in any relationship and that is what contributes towards its success and I can't deny that I 100% agree. And no it's not just a romantic relationship that this rule applies to – it applies to any relationship that is worth existing; whether it be a child and their parent, two best friends, a pair of siblings or one that is professional relationship.

At times we throw away a relationship because we expect the other person to understand what we need and expect from them and when they don't we spontaneously decide that they aren't the one for us. None of us stop and think that maybe they would know if we actually told them and expressed how we felt and told them about our expectations. The truth is no one is psychic or a mind reader. And we can't expect people to do exactly what we expect from them. Because truth is expectations and only leads to disappointments. And more than that they hurt... especially when we're let down by those we considered our loved ones, those closest to our hearts, those we trusted with our lives – hence, it's best not to have any. To just live life, take each day as it comes – if something good happens take it as a pleasant surprise – at least that way you won't feel let down if someone hasn't done or said as you expected from them.

There is someone I really wish would talk to me, there is so much we both need to say to each other; whether it be an apology, expressing how much we've missed each other or felt without each other. At times ego and lack of communication breaks down not only a relationship but a person as well. It completely destroys them to the point where they don't believe in anything anymore and stop expecting anything from life. And that is when you know something inside them has died.

We really take life for granted – human nature they call it – but we really are ungrateful species who only think about ourselves rather than taking into consideration facts of life – it is too short, time never comes back and once you lose someone; don't let it get too late. I don't see the point in holding grudges, I have always tried my best to give people a second, third, even a bloody fourth chance, but there comes a time in life where you've got to stop being selfless and put yourself first and think about your poor heart because let me tell you... No one else will!

Life is way too short to put anything on tomorrow, no matter how big or small – do a good deed today rather than tomorrow, fix a ruined friendship today rather than tomorrow, apologise to someone who's been hurt today rather than tomorrow and most of all tell someone you love them today, right now rather than tomorrow! Because you never know... whether tomorrow will come or not – after all tomorrow is never promised!

Talk to those around you – those that are still alive – living with regrets while visiting them in graveyards and talking to the graves is much harder than going to someone's face and expressing how you feel.

Wish you were here...

No matter how much we deny it we all need someone, that is the reason apparently God has made us in pairs. As they say, 'the One', the one that we all search for all our lives, the one who is supposed to be our life partner. The one who is meant to be by our sides for the rest of our lives till death do us part.

I wish he was here... my very own 'the one' so to say... or just someone who'd be my everything... someone who'd always be there for me. Someone who'll support me no matter what, when the whole world may turn against me.

Many a time we live in a rather fantasy world where we believe everything will work out and you end up with the very perfect person who will give you all the happiness in the world.

But the truth is; that doesn't always happen in real life. Fairy tales and crazy fantasies aren't very practical now are they? Prince charming doesn't always come on a beautiful white horse when a damsel is in distress and needs him the most.

Serendipity – an occurrence or development of events that happen by chance in an unexpected way that ends in happiness. That is how in most cases you meet the one; he comes when you least expect it or rather when you aren't even looking. There's a saying: When one door shuts, God opens up another one. Or sometimes sunshine comes in through a window you didn't even know you had left open.

There are good days and bad days... days when you lose hope and faith in everything and on good days you experience that once in a lifetime kind of happiness and wish you had someone to share it with. Someone to hold your hand whilst you both watch the sunset on the beaches of Thailand, or to applaud for you when you finally get that degree you worked your ass off for or to be there by your side at 1am when you're studying for that goddamn accounting exam.

I wish you were here so that I didn't feel so alone, so that we could support each other and be there for each other. Wish you were here so we could watch sunsets together, be on the phone whilst looking at the stars through our respective windows, to motivate each other in our different careers and life aspirations, to pick each other up when things go from bad to worse. To inspire each other for things that we believe in, for things we want to do but are too scared to do.

I just wish you were here...

I Still Miss You...

I still miss you... yes still... I never thought I would... after all when does it stop? Will it even ever stop? Waiting for the day I stop missing you. It's not just the simple I miss you; it's the I miss you that causes a sharp pain in my chest, wishing you were here, wishing I could do something anything, to make this pain go away.

Why do I still miss you? A question I ask myself every single day, every single moment of absolute melancholy that I feel. But to no avail. Just a question unanswered. An emotion not dealt with. A pile of feelings buried deep down.

People don't understand and never can understand something they've not experienced and I mean how can you even expect them too? I get asked how I can still miss you after everything that happened... the pain you caused my weak little heart, the way you destroyed my soul and left my body bruised and most of all left me damaged.

I never quite understood how we as humans have the capability to miss a person who caused us nothing but hurt and misery; whether it be a lover or a best friend.

There's this constant heavy weight on my chest that I feel every single moment of every day, causing an ache that urges me to talk to you, to tell you how I feel and just how much I miss you, just how much I wish you were here... by my side to help make things better.

What's even worse than missing someone is not being able to tell them, not being able to talk to them and share your feelings? A misconception about missing someone is also that you only miss someone when you're all alone, or at night when you can't seem to sleep. Let me enlighten you that that isn't missing someone, that is when you feel lonely. Because missing someone is in the midst of a really busy day at work, or a really crowded club while you're on a night out with friends or when just a song can bring back a thousand memories and make you miss that one special person.

Why is it that I still miss you?

I miss you annoying me with little things, miss you teasing me, the way you stared at me while I made my silly cute face that you loved, I miss the way you used to eat up all my favourite ice cream while apparently have bought it for me. Miss those late night chats about anything and everything. Miss your jealous moods when a guy would look at me or compliment me. Your drunken phases where you'd turn into an absolute baby to deal with.

Why is it that I miss every tiny detail about you, about us despite the bad outweighing the good by more than a mile? Why? Why is it that despite me still hurting because of the way you broke me I still miss the very few happy moments we had?

Waiting for the day I don't miss you anymore... you know why because I am sick of saying and realizing that I still miss you. Waiting for the day I don't feel this pain anymore, waiting for the day I don't have to carry this burden around with me anymore. Waiting for the day what you did in the past doesn't impact my future anymore.

A Starbucks Experience

Sitting at a Starbucks sipping on my usual order – a delicious mocha light Frappuccino and yes no whipped cream on top. Can't stand it.

A Starbucks experience brings back so many memories for me; in regards to the different Starbucks I've been fortunate enough to have an experience at around the world, the different varieties it offers to different target markets around the globe but most of all because of the many different experiences I've had at the coffee maker's inn.

From my very first date with my college sweetheart, the every week catch up Frappuccino with my best friend to the surprise birthday for my first love. Starbucks has had a rather special place in my heart; a place where I've made up with long lost friends, had a girly chat after shopping with mum to sitting at one all by myself working on my university work, slogging away on life.

I still remember the times I used to meet up with a so called best friend at the time almost every other day just to hang out and de-stress after a long day at university, during the winter where she'd order a mocha latte and I'd order a mocha Frappuccino and she'd always tell me off for having a frozen drink during the winter. Then, as always I'd joke about how she was cold and I was hot and hence our drinks had to be of the opposite temperature. The laughs we used to have will stay in our hearts forever, because eventually she did prove how cold she was inside to betray a friend.

My actual best friend today of many years and I have shared many great experiences at the coffee giant as well, from having a coffee doze to keep us awake at airports before and after many of our adventures that we've had together, to just having a catch up after work about how life has been since the last time we've met which at times has been just two days and on other occasions two weeks.

One that I will never forget was my very first date with my college sweetheart; a fellow college mate who absolutely adored me, at the time we were both at college and eventually we ended up dating and having our very first date at Starbucks sharing our favourite drinks and favourite stories about college life and he complained about how I never gave him the time or the day back then. We ended up together four years after the poor guy had asked me out. We had also shared a yummylicious chocolate brownie (my favourite must have) when we had met there on New Year's Eve; part of my early birthday celebration as I was about to leave the country before it.

One of my best memories I would have to say is when I had surprised my first love at Starbucks on his birthday. He had been late and I was very annoyed and did not speak a word to him while walking there though he kept questioning where I was taking him. While patiently waiting for me and watching the instructions I gave the barista, I still to the day remember the smile he had on his face which only grew bigger when the barista brought out a hot chocolate with a smiley face on it along with a slice of delicious and scrumptious cake with happy birthday written on the side with caramel sauce. I wish

I had a better phone camera back then to have captured that moment but it's safely stored in my heart so I can re-watch it whenever I want. The genuine smile that reflected pure happiness on his face is one I will never forget. Celebrating his birthday with him on his actual day meant a lot to me, always has and I'm glad I had the opportunity to do it at one of my favourite places.

Starbucks – It's been a place full of memories, luckily I can say only great ones; laughs, tears of joys, celebrations and just pure happiness. A place that kind of feels like home everywhere I see it. Whether it is in a country where I've travelled to alone, of which there's been many, to one where I've lived alone for a long period of time and Starbucks has been an escape. There have been many of them where I've sat in through my student life working my life away on assignments, presentations and most importantly my dissertation.

I actually wrote my very first blog at a Starbucks in Thailand... so there you have it.

Just another place with a box full of happy memories. Memories are like a box of chocolates; once you open the box you can't just have one piece. So there it is, my pieces of chocolates at Starbucks while I sit here yet again sipping on my Mocha light Frappuccino.

The thought of you...

All I could think about today was you...

Five years ago today we spoke to each other after a very long time and today, all I could think about was you... I wanted to speak to you again; after all we always went back to each other. I wonder why I still miss you... I wonder why the spark... our spark never went away. As much as I was yearning to talk to you... I couldn't... so much has happened. How do you look at someone you truly love and agree it's time to walk away?

Walking away from you... every single time that I have had to do it has been the hardest thing ever. Harder than living alone in a foreign country, harder than not being able to communicate in a foreign language, harder than getting over a car crash that nearly killed me, harder than losing someone that kept me sane, harder than the betrayal of a best friend. I miss you... yes I still do... despite everything you've done. Despite all the pain, the lies, the betrayal and the broken promises. No matter how much pain there was; we did have a lot of happy moments. Moments I know I still cherish... and somewhere deep down I know you do too.

I don't know why the thought of you has really been bugging me today. Every little thing has reminded me of you today or a memory associate with you... even a small and meaningless thing like a pen. It was from a place we had visited together.

A decade – a rather long time but that is how long we've known each other now. Been in and out of each other's life. Thinking about the memories of sharing our birthdays together brought a tear to my eyes today just while sitting with a bunch of friends at a dinner party. Amazing how you can still have that impact on me. How the memories we shared can still make my heart sink in the midst of a busy environment. The thought of loving you broke me once again today... and all I wanted was to talk to you and tell you...

Melancholia

Ever felt so numb and broken that you reach a point that you become silent? It's almost like you reach the death of silence. Not a silence where you can't speak but one where you can't cry. Tears – a fluid created in the human eye from experiencing an emotion caused by stress, anger, sadness and suffering physical as well as emotional pain.

Ever sat there and felt a sharp pain in your chest that you can't control. Emotions that are spiralling out of control.

But still... no tears. Why is it that I can't cry? Why is it that no tears want to come and fall out despite the pain killing me inside causing me a slow melancholic death. A death that couldn't come sooner. Tears are known are to be good... they are a thundershower for the soul. They seem to clear out the toxins from our body, clear our eyes of the bad memories and of everything that is clouding our judgement. As hard as it may seem sometimes all you can do is cry. But that doesn't make you a weak person nor does it make you a coward – so never ever stop yourself from crying because there are some people who are so unfortunate that they can't cry... not a single tear. When you've had an overflow of pain and suffering... sometimes your eyes dry out... the waterfall stops and there's nothing left but agony.

Agony that you live with – an agony that is supposed to die down with time as they say but who knows. Today... after a long time I really want to cry it out... the pain I'm holding in together but I can't.

Frustrated yet smiling.

Ten years – A decade – A lifetime

Feels weird to say that it's been a decade. Feels like a lifetime for me. Ten years ago... exactly today my whole life changed. Something I had never ever expected to happen even in my wildest dreams. After all a 16-year-old doesn't expect a stranger to change her whole life in just the blink of an eye.

It was my first day at work, my first step in the real world, I was super excited and ecstatic about this new chapter in my life, but little did I know God had a completely different new chapter written for me. While working on one of the shop floor shelves, another new starter came up to me and started a conversation; instantly we had a spark, his smile quickly matched mine, the sparkle in his eyes quickly travelled to mine; the chemistry between us lit like a fire between our bodies.

In just a day we became inseparable; we had a special connection, a spark that still ignites between us even today, ten years later. A decade is a very long time, people change, feelings fade away, love dies and the fire between two lovers gets put out; but that wasn't the case with us.

We've had many ups and downs in this lifetime of a journey that we've been through together, but mostly not together, but what kept bringing us back to each other was our spark. Though there was an underlying love he was unwilling to accept, we both always deeply cared for each other and wanted the best for one another.

Two people only connected through a spark... a spark that never went away. A spark that kept bringing them back together no matter where they were in the world or where they ended up. After all what kind of spark was this? A spark that kept bringing two people together despite them never actually coming together as a couple or as lovers. A spark ignited in both their hearts and shone through on their faces whenever they came face to face. A spark that pushed them towards each other. A spark that never stopped them from caring for each other, worrying about each other and despite them not knowing but loving each other. What kind of spark was this?

It's been ten years today but not a single day has gone by that I haven't asked myself as to why he came into my life? Why did he make me fall in love with him? Why did I end up caring about him so much when I had no right on him and still don't? Why do I still care about him to the point where I put him first even before my own wellbeing? At times people come into our lives as a blessing whereas others as a lesson. I guess he was a lesson, a lesson to never trust everything someone says. A lesson to not expect honesty from anyone just because honesty is one of the principals of your life. I guess that's what he was for me.

Having fallen in love with someone who didn't love me back in return has changed me as a person. In fact that one person that I met 10 years ago today has completely changed my life forever. The girl who loved this guy deeply, truly and unconditionally doesn't believe in love anymore. The girl who did everything for him just to make him realize her love for him doesn't justify her emotions to anyone anymore. The girl who did everything to express her emotions to him, her love and her care for him doesn't express anything anymore. The bubbly ray of sunshine doesn't smile anymore, doesn't express her feelings anymore and doesn't love anymore.

They say unrequited love is the best kind of love because only one person has power over their love... and that is you. You don't have to be with someone to truly love them. But I don't agree... I'd rather never had fallen in love than had loved someone who didn't love me back. I'd rather never had fallen in love than had loved someone who didn't know the meaning of the word. I'd rather never had fallen in love than had loved someone who only broke me and left me destroyed.

Ten years later... it still hurts. The brick on my chest that doesn't seem to lift, the lump in my throat that doesn't seem to shift, the pain in my heart that doesn't seem to leave me alone and most of all the tears in my eyes that don't seem to want to stop. Ten years later... broken, destroyed and numb... I still love you.

CHAPTER 4: THE TRAVEL BUG

She's a Globetrotter!

This girl has the travel bug... she can't stay in one place for long... or shall I say for more than a month at a time... she feels the urge strongly not only to travel but to move... move away from her comfort zone... move away from normality... move away from everyday life.

She travels... not to escape life but so that life does not escape her. This might appear shocking to you but this girl isn't scared of death... she embraces death like she would a loved one. She jokes around... "I'm not scared of death you people, what actually scares me is true love".

Though she says this life is a rather long journey where she has many dreams that she wants to turn into reality, many challenges she wants to accomplish and many goals that she wants to fulfil. However, she also believes in the present... that life actually is too short! If you want to do something, do it now, if you want to achieve a goal, now's the time... make a plan and go for it, if you want to tell someone you love them, do it now! Don't wait for the time when they aren't in this world anymore, if you want to travel... do it now! Look up flights... book them and get packing.

That's how Miss Independent lives – she's a crazy girl who once left home scared, worried and very unwell to do something she never thought she was capable of. Teaching; I mean who does that? That too in another country where they don't speak English – this little madam decided to go and teach English. The naughtiest student at school who always got in trouble with the teacher, never did her homework on time and failed most of the mathematics test in her school life, was now going to go TEACH English in another country. That's who she is... crazy, spontaneous, adventurous... she does things at times without thinking how she will actually execute them. But like one of her exes always said to her – she was 'superwoman'. A girl who never gave up no matter how tough the situation, no matter how intricately someone broke her or how lost she felt in this big bad world.

Travelling the world is what made her who she is today – a confident, fearless, independent young woman who doesn't need anyone. She believes in her God and that's all she needs.

She feels blessed enough to have the ability and resources to travel the world at such a young age, at times with friends, with family, with her love or the best ones – just with herself.

Forgotten the number of countries she has travelled to... she still has a list of the ones she still wants to see, feel and explore. Anyone would say, the one thing this girl truly and deeply loves with a passion is to travel.

Once you travel, you never quite feel at home anymore because there are parts of you in each country, city, place, street that you have been to and there are so many that are waiting for another part of you.

Travelling the world, she says, has made her so much more open and accepting in life. She is willing to try new things a lot more than ever before. This is the girl who jumped off the highest hotel in Berlin – ALONE. Who does that? She finds it strange when she sees people unwilling to travel without their so-called friends. She smiles to herself and thinks what a disadvantage it is to have to depend on someone and at times her heart wishes she had someone she could depend on but then she looks back on her journey and smiles again. Looks up at her God and smiles... I know I'll have that someone one day and then I might never travel alone again... so until then... let's continue.

NYC... I'll never get over you; Part 1

New York is the meeting place of the people, the only city where you can hardly find a typical American. They say one belongs to New York instantly; one belongs to it as much in five minutes as in five years.

Summer 2015 – A crazy, independent, fun loving globe trotter moved to New York... the city that they say never sleeps. Funnily enough exactly four years after she had been to the city for the first time. Back then, that was a simple family holiday with her parents. But this... she wasn't quite sure what this was. Was it simply a new adventure? A wise career move? Another opportunity to travel and see another part of the world? Or was it just an escape from herself?

She moved her whole life to New York and decided to live as a brand new New Yorker for the year; moving was already a norm for her but this time she wasn't running away... she knew what she wanted and that is exactly what she went after. She was a determined, owl vision focused and very independent young woman; someone who claimed to love her once taunted her as 'superwoman'. That normally would be seen as a compliment. But this was said out of frustration. She was so used to not depending on anyone and dealing with everything all by herself that this way of life of hers was alien to most and hence, one day this lover frustrated with her silence of hiding all her pain demanded, "you should really stop acting like a superwoman all the time!" But he didn't know that life had made her that way.

Times Square, Macy's, the Bronx, the Flushing Meadows Park, Brooklyn Bridge, George Washington Bridge, the Empire State Building, Williamsburg, the World Trade Centre, Wall Street and her absolute favourite – the Hudson; from where she often stared at the much loved and talked about Manhattan skyline were her life for a year.

She was always a city girl, but little did she know that she was going to become a Wall Street girl one day... working on Wall

Street – a dream every business minded individual wishes would become reality. And there she was a successful businesswoman of the future.

Wall Street girl by day... a party animal by night and lots more in the middle... whether it was hitting the gym religiously, grabbing coffee with her American Bae (and the bestest friend a girl could ask for in a new country), FaceTiming her parents, listening to the crisis in the lives of her close friends back home, dealing with love – she did it all and managed it pretty well... after all someone once said – she was 'superwoman'.

Independence brings with itself a load of responsibility. An apartment in New York, dealing with the horrible subways, busy streets, managing chores, bills, relationships, work and anything that life throws at you can be a lot – let alone in a whole new country.

It was intense to say the least – but an experience that'll live with her for life. The best, worst and everything in between is what has made her into what she is today. An ex-Wall Street girl still taking over the world and pursuing her dream, living with passion and awaiting love.

While travelling... you meet angels

Travelling... makes me happy! It's not about going to a new place or running away from an old one but it's everything that happens in between. The planning... the excitement when I pack... the time before the flight that always goes slowly... and the happy yet uncertain moment as soon as my feet hit the ground in a new land.

I always believe that travelling isn't just about the new places that you see but so much more about the people that you meet. Some inspire you... some annoy you of course; but the ones that turn into lifelong friends are the ones that make you smile years down the line, when you look back on the memories that you created together in a country that belongs to none of you... but what does belong to both of you is the experience that you shared together in that foreign country – whether it was at the beach, at the bar, at the club, at a temple in Asia, at a tattoo place in Vegas, at a sports bar in Brussels, at a hostel in San Francisco, at a restaurant in New York or simply on a tour bus or boat anywhere in the world. You shared it together and made those memories. I always hate getting a tan... I'm Asian, it's in my blood not to like the idea of getting darker but I always believe that though tan lines fade... the memories last forever.

My tan from Miami... though it has faded now and has been replaced by the one I've got in Thailand but the memories live forever. Today I made a new memory through making a new friend... a six-year-old Singaporean girl who became friends with me on a cruise boat on the way to an island in Thailand. She kept talking to me and making me smile; I guess I hadn't been smiling due to feeling unwell. But that's the thing about kids... they make you forget all your troubles. She also asked me if I was a child or a teen... little did she know I was an adult... funnily enough she said something I get a lot – "I sound like a little girl" – I guess along with having a baby face... I also have a young voice. But that little girl taught me something I guess I teach people without even knowing – to face your fears.

So the situation was that we had stopped in the middle of the sea for swimming and relaxing as part of the tour – however, as it wasn't a proper beach and we were told that the water is deep and has all sorts of sea fish that could be dangerous, I was a bit hesitant to jump in. Additionally to the fact that when I had tried snorkelling two days ago – my breathing had been playing up as I suffer from asthma. However, the little girl very bravely jumped into the water and kept persuading me and pushing me to jump in. I did step down at first but when I went under the water... I couldn't feel like I could stay in so I jumped back out. However, after lots of pushing and persuasion... very scared I jumped in again, just for her... she was so sweet about it and I didn't want to let her down but more than that I didn't want to let myself down... and yes I went under the water yet again but after a while as she held my hand and very sweetly said, "See... it's fun isn't it?" everything was okay... I started enjoying myself while forgetting how dirty the water was or feeling fearful of jellyfish. I finally faced my fear and even enjoyed myself.

Sometimes when we're down in the dumps... even if humans who know you or don't know you don't realize... God does; and he sends an angel to help you get back up... the little girl was my angel that day who made me smile and also made me realize just how strong I am... as I very conveniently forget sometimes. I am glad I jumped in as I did not want to come out at the end and most importantly because deep down I know I would have regretted it... and one thing you'll learn about me is that I don't do regrets.

Airports

There's a thing about airports; mixed feelings... it's a happy as well as sad place for many. Airports – where some wait impatiently to see their loved ones after what could range from days to years... on the other hand, where some say goodbye to those close to the heart... again at times just for a short period of time... or sometimes for life.

Airports always bring a smile to my face but ignite an ache in my heart too when I see the two types of people experiencing either immense happiness or heartache. It's amazing how the two emotions are on extremes... it hurts a lot to see those you love go away... whether it's by choice or for work or leisure... the uncertainty of not knowing whether or not you'll see them again hurts... often kills. Thanks to recent incidents regarding plane crashes – it has made the saying 'life is very unpredictable' even more believable.

On the other hand, waiting at the airport arrivals hall for the one you love – is one of the most beautiful feelings in the world; with flowers in your hand and a hundred thoughts of what you'll do with them first or where you'll take them. Some of us stop thinking after the point we're in their arms... hugging them tightly... to never let them go again. There was a time I stood in the departure hall... holding your hand... crying my heart out... knowing that you're leaving and that I might never see you again was killing me... even if I had a cold hearted bitch face on for most of the time.

Letting that hand go just before you joined the security queue... broke me. I wish I never said goodbye... but I guess... if you're brave enough to say goodbye... life will reward you with a new hello... though I was brave enough, or at least pretended to be brave enough to say goodbye to you... I'm still standing at that same point for life to reward me with a new hello.

Airports – places that also makes me happy knowing where I've been and where I'm heading to next, but the best feeling is when you know you're heading home... because no matter where you go in life; home is home at the end of the day. The comfort you feel in your own bed, the food that your parents serve you that has love with every bite, the familiarity around you, the loving arms of your mother and the feeling of being home doesn't compare to the most beautiful beaches, luxurious hotels, crazy casinos, beautiful sceneries or the unreal places this earth has to offer to us.

There's just so much that happens at an airport, some people are going away for work, some to see their family, some to study/work abroad and then there are those that just travel. Because truth is you'll always make money... but you can't always make memories. Here's me sitting at an airport for the third time in a week, thinking about what's next... where I'm heading to and where I'll be heading the next time I'll be at an airport.

Solo Travel = Happiness

Travel is the only thing you buy that makes you richer. When people ask me what I do in my spare time or what is the one thing

I love doing? The answer that always comes to mind is 'travelling' whether it's in casual conversation or in a job interview.

And solo travel my friend is the best – because not only does solo travel push you out of your comfort zone, but it also pushes you out of the zone of the expectations of others. When you travel solo it's just you and yourself and of course your suitcase. It's all about you, what you want to do with your day or don't want to do with your day, you don't have to follow someone else's schedule or plans. You're free to do whatever you like and to see whatever it is you want to explore.

Having been blessed enough to see quite a bit of the world solo as well as with friends and family, I can say that solo travel was one of the best experiences of my life, not having to worry about anything or anyone else is just the best. My first solo travel was to the Great Wall of China and even though it was a trip I took against my parents' wishes, it was one of the best and even today when I look back, it makes me smile as well as makes me pinch myself at times not being able to believe that I actually travelled half way across the world on my first ever solo adventure.

Climbing the Great Wall of China when I was only 19 was an amazing yet surreal experience. I still remember it was absolutely boiling hot in China at the time as it was their peak summer season and i had finished all my water half way across the wall and I had started feeling dizzy due to my anaemia. However, thankfully there was a shop along the way, which saved my life.

Staying at the hotel alone, going to the pool, using the spa in my own time and leisure felt so good... and really relaxing after a long day in the heat. Sometimes it takes to be alone to realize just how much fun being alone can be. I am a true believer of being able to be happy within yourself, because if you can't be happy with yourself, then it's very difficult for you to be happy with another person. I don't like and understand people who always want to be with someone, I think it is a privilege for one to enjoy one's own company.

My next trip alone was when I decided to move to Germany for a year, all by myself. That was a huge one. I never thought, I would ever do something like that, just based on my personality and whom I was as a child growing up; a shy, introvert girl who lacked confidence big time. But hey life happens, and you change... or should I say life changes you. Living alone in a completely new country where I didn't even speak the language at the time was a huge challenge, but on the contrary, it was my own adventure and that too a year long. It was incredible, I got to travel around the country and visited one of the most beautiful cities in Germany called Heidelberg and as the Germans call it, 'Ich habe mein Herz in Heidelberg verloren', which translates to 'I lost my heart in Heidelberg'.

And my most recent solo travel was to Vietnam. Surprising? I know right... it's a country, I don't know why, but I never thought I'd go to or more that I would ever be able to go to. But I am so glad that I did... It was incredibly beautiful. I absolutely fell in love with the country... I went straight to the capital, Hanoi – stayed at Old Square... a very antique looking neighbourhood that was right in the middle of the city centre and next to its very beautiful and scenic Hoan Kiem lake, where I went every night just to chill at the end of a long day or sometimes slow day... just to gather my thoughts or to look up at the sky and thank God for all the opportunities that He has given me in life, especially the ones to travel the world.

There are many more stories and perhaps I'll do an individual blog for each country, but for now... a piece of advice, no matter what's going on in your life, take a breath and just think about travelling... alone. As Akon said... "I'm riding solo," trust me it'll be the best decision and time of your life.

Chicago–o–o The Windy City

Chicago is famously known as 'The Windy City' for the obvious reason of being too windy and cold and exactly this

time last year two people insanely in love went there to celebrate the birthday of someone very special. It was the birthday
of the man she loved, they both flew to Chicago together for
his special birthday weekend. It wouldn't be a lie to say she
was more excited for his birthday than he was. Not because
they were going to be in a new place and it would be a mini
holiday but more because she couldn't wait to give him his
presents, after all she had ran around looking after each tiny
detail for every present; from the card to the present to the
chocolates. It was so cold in Chicago... as soon as they landed...
especially after she was so hung-over from the night before.
But they were happy... they were happy because he was happy...
his happiness meant a lot for her... but what was said was that
he never understood that.

He was her pizza baby and she took him to a very famous
deep-dish pizza place called 'Giordanos' for his birthday meal.
He loved pizza, sometimes she felt that he loved pizza more
than her and would always tease him about it. But deep-dish
pizza really was the best pizza they had both ever had. Seeing
him have it made her fall in love with him all over again. And
then as she always was; full of surprises, she made an excuse
about going to the loo but went to the bar and ordered a piece
of chocolate cake for him... another one of both of their
favourites and was gone for quite a while. She came back with
some cake with a lit candle on it and surprised him... He was
so ecstatic! He didn't expect anything like that from her...
especially not such a sweet gesture.

Chicago was a cold place that brought two people in love
even closer... it made his cold heart towards her warm again,
simply because away from everything and everyone he could
finally see her for who she is and for every single thing she did
for him on his birthday weekend.

Exactly this time last year... two people in love were on their
way to Chicago... a weekend away from life... a weekend of
love and birthday celebrations. Amazing how time flies by...
amazing how things change... circumstances don't stay the

same and most of all how people reveal their true colours either by hurting you or leaving you.

A lot can happen in a year... from being in Chicago to now just being lost...

It's just a place... with a lifetime of memories

The Hudson is a 315-mile long river that flows from north to south primarily through eastern New York.

A place that became my happy place or rather my escape while New York was a temporary home... it was the most peaceful place ever that I could find in the entire city, a city known to never sleep – a city full of hustle and bustle, huge parties, busy streets and all kinds of crazy people.

While living in New York; there were many times I found myself by the Hudson River, especially because I lived a two-minute walk from it, but mainly because it was the only place in the whole city where I felt at peace. Whether I was alone or with someone... standing by the river always felt so serene. I remember times where I've stood there all alone; with tears in my eyes at times longing for love or at other times missing home on special occasions. At times just taking a moment to be alone, to not be surrounded by hustle and bustle and just to take a moment to look up at the sky and to thank God for everything good in life.

I spent the evening talking to someone who started off by being a stranger by the river to going on to becoming an amazing friend. Another evening with someone who pretended to be a best friend; and another one with someone who pretended to be the love of my life. But in all honesty the best ones were the ones I spent alone... walking by the river... taking a moment to myself amongst the jungle.

There are always certain places in life that make you stop and catch your breath every time you walk past them; not only because they hold a special place in your heart but mainly because they store a lifetime of memories for you – memories that make you smile out of the blue, or at times bring a tear to your eye.

That's exactly what the Hudson River was for me – a very special place that holds a special significance to my life during some of the most changing months in my life that have shaped me into the person I am today.

A place that holds bittersweet connotation – but will always hold a very special place in my heart.

NYC... I'll never get over you - Part 2

One belongs to New York instantly; one belongs to it in five minutes as in five years. Such is New York City – it makes you its own without having done anything. It is a city very close to my heart having lived there and built a home. A city that taught me a lot, from how to cook every day, managing a full-time job along with studying for a Master's degree along with managing a relationship with those that I had left back home.

From taking walks in Central Park, aimlessly exploring Times Square to working on Wall Street at one of the tallest buildings in New York next to the World Trade Centre. Being able to see Brooklyn Bridge from Wall Street is a view that I'll never forget simply because it is a view I had fallen in love with at first sight.

Walking through Central Park, one can not only get lost in such a maze of greenery but also meet people from all different walks of life regardless of their colour and background. It is a meeting point for many, for some a place to hang out in the summer and for others a place to play sports and exercise before or after work. A beautiful area with abundance of not just nature and people but unique architecture from the steps that lead to the world famous fountain that turns to ice in the winter to the archway where many kisses have been shared amongst friends that have turned into lovers.

The way out of Central Park can lead to Fifth Avenue, a street known for its prestigious shopping and tourist attractions. A street I always watched in films and always wondering what it would be like to walk down it and fortunately I had the opportunity to do so. Shoppers of all kinds fill the avenue from those that carry Chanel handbags to those that are happy with buying from H&M and Uniqlo.

World famous Times Square – my absolute favourite spot in the big apple, not because of its hustle bustle and never ending lights but because of the feelings I have whenever I'm there – feeling ecstatic and full of life from the energy of the place filled with people from all over the world. Known as a major commercial intersection and one of the most populated tourist attractions in the world, filled with many yellow cabs, which are next to impossible to hail, it stretches from the 42nd Street and goes up until the 47th Street. It is a place that felt good not only after work for dinner or drinks but also after a night out when it was absolutely empty glowing with the endless coloured billboards lighting up the place.

Another favourite spot in New York I would say is Greenwich Village – perfect for a typical night out in New York where I've shared some of the best nights out with true friends in the big apple. Bleecker Street being one of our main hang out spots for a Saturday night and sometimes even on a Friday night straight after work. Bar hopping, endless rounds and the variety of shots available truly made it an experience of nightlife in NYC to remember. And of course how can I forget the Dollar Slice ritual after every single night out accomplished in the city that never sleeps. It can be eaten before or after a night out; before to have a layer of something in your stomach before you drown it with alcohol and after, to absorb all the drinking that has now been done. There were times, nights out in the area that took place on a weeknight and work was reached hung-over. But those are the days and especially the memories that you don't forget.

An important lesson learnt in NYC – You'll regret more the things that you didn't do than the ones you did.

And lastly I have to say a place in NYC that always felt like home to me was Brooklyn Bridge – not solely because I absolutely love bridges but also it was a place that calmed me down when I felt anxious, made me feel at home when I missed home and was always there – a view I had from near my desk at work.

IF you're a globetrotter – there will always be a special place in every country that you have visited that will feel like home.

CHAPTER 5: FORGIVENESS

Water under the bridge...

They say the weak can never forgive. Forgiveness is the attribute of the strong. If someone apologises sincerely and genuinely... you can forgive him or her. Forgiving someone who has wronged you is not necessarily for them... but for you... for your sanity... for your wellbeing... for your peace of mind... so your broken heart can be at peace. But... how do you forgive someone who isn't even sorry? Sorry for breaking you... for destroying your soul... for leaving those broken pieces on the floor and just staring down at them in arrogance rather than help you putting them back together.

I guess if forgiveness is the attribute of the strong... not asking for forgiveness is a flaw of the weak. The weak may feel belittled when in a situation to ask for pardon... for wronging someone... even when that someone is a friend or a loved one. There are people out there that claim to love you 'to the moon and back' and worship the ground that you walk on... however, love isn't just words... it needs actions. If someone cannot ask you for forgiveness for almost destroying you or at least attempting to... then do they really love you? Did they really mean everything they said? Were those feelings real? What was the ulterior motive behind that pretence; love? Who knows? I guess I'll never know. But I forgive you... even though you're not sorry... I do. And not for you... but for me... so I can finally let go of you... let go of the feelings... attempt to erase the happy memories... kill all the hopes and just let go. And you know what, I know you never wanted me to, but today... I have let you go.

E for Ego

They say E for Ego ruins the best of relationships as well as people.

This is a story about exactly that. His ego was ruining not only him but his relationships around him. He was a very selfish man... he only ever thought about himself and not anyone else. Not his parents or his siblings or his friends and most of all not her.

He knew he needed her... she made him whole again. She brought that smile back to his face, which finally matched the sparkle in his eyes. She was everything he wanted. He never knew it until he met her but... she was.

She could make him smile without doing anything, her pretty face used to make him smile, her cute expressions made him happy and her unintentional actions that portrayed only love and care made him feel like the luckiest man on this earth.

But his ego was too big, as they say male ego is a killer and he was stupid and blind enough to let it get in the way of everything. His life, his happiness and her.

He loved her, to the moon and back he claimed; yet wanted to own her. She was his love not a slave. You can't own people and that's where he went wrong. The girl who made him whole was the one he broke. Just because of his big ego, his selfish nature and his insecurities.

Now he's burning in the fire of his own ego. He's hurting but won't admit it. Instead he'll light a cigarette, one after and another. Hoping smoking them will take the pain away, but they don't. Every time he lights them... he sees her face in every flame because she had always forbidden him from smoking. She cared way too much about him, especially his health.

Ego comes along with a lot of anger and hatred. His anger and hatred towards her not only broke her but also is now slowly killing him. He misses her but won't admit it, he's sorry but won't ever apologise and most of all he's hurting but won't express it.

Don't let poisons such as your anger and ego ruin the one you claim to love and your relationships. Loving your ego won't get you far in life. Relationships need love, respect and compassion.

Regrets... &... Reminders

Life is too short to live it with any kind of regrets. But the bitter truth of life is that life is filled with regrets and often they come with reminders. Regrets are a part and parcel of life – and often it is those things that we regret that we don't do, rather than the things that we actually do. I always lived a life without regrets, always said that I don't have any regrets in life but all that changed when I met you. You became my biggest regret in life – running away as they say doesn't get anyone anywhere in life, and I wish I hadn't – running away from unrequited love hurts, kills and destroys a person and I was human after all.

A completely broken and lifeless soul she was; there was no life in her body – she could be called a living corpse; with no feelings or emotion, someone who had been bled dry of tears. She had been through hell and back and always came out the other end – but not this time, this time you completely broke her, destroyed that last ounce of hope she was holding onto, or rather that hope was the only thing keeping her alive. You came like a saviour in her life, a knight in shining armour; saving the girl who was happily standing at deaths door embracing her with both arms but you pulled her back! Little did she know that rather than saving her from death, you were saving her only to live a life that was worse than death. Who does that? Who breaks the one they claim to love? Who destroys the soul that opened up to them? Like who does that? The worse thing about regrets is that they come with a lifetime of reminders – reminders of the good times that turned out to be fake – reminders of all the happy memories that according to you were just a pretence. I can't even fake a hello yet you faked a love that is only one of a kind; only those lucky in life or importantly in love are fortunately enough to have that.

You were an unpleasant memory; but now you're my reminder. You're my reminder to be more cautious of the people I invest my time in. You're my reminder to see people as who they are, and not who I want them to be. You're my reminder to fall in love with how people treat me, not what they tell me. But if by chance I do fall for the wrong person again, you are my reminder that I can survive the worst.

"I'm sorry I cheated... " she said.

Ever felt the dark clouds filled with lies, betrayal and manipulation clear away from your eyes once the toxic person has exited your life? That's what happens when you let go of the bad and accept the good in your life. The negative people that only cause drama and chaos in your life are the ones that once gone allow you to actually see the ones that bring positivity to your life, the ones that bring a smile to your face, the ones that are truly happy for you when good things happen and stand by you in your times of need.

She was the love of your life, someone you waited a very long time to be yours, the best day of your life you said was when you 'made her mine'. She was your cutie, your babe and your piece of hotness as you used to call her. But she was also this girl who was in love with a player. The player who was the first guy ever that she had liked and developed feelings for. Was it her fault that he turned out to be a player? Someone not even worthy of being called a human being; he was as heartless as a stone, colder than snow and more lifeless than an artificial plant.

But she still loved him with every bone in her body; with every breath she took, with every smile she wore and with every day that she lived. Without reason her love just grew for him with each passing day. Not that he deserved any of it. But it wasn't up to her. She tried everything in her power to forget him, forget her love for him, to move on. To move on and be with you. Someone who actually loved her for who she was. She did feel for you and adore you for the amazing, loving and gentle being that you were. But she had only ever loved one person and that wasn't you. It was that one weak moment, that moment where she completely lost herself, not that she wasn't lost before, but his birthday was always a time she would be at her weakest; especially during times where she had to forcefully stop herself from wishing him. She had to stop herself from going back to him again.

She was wrong that year. She pushed you away from herself on his birthday. She was alone. Incapable of dealing with the pain tearing up her chest and due to her selfless nature she didn't want to burden you with her melancholy. You were the only good thing in her life back then. The only positivity. The only person who could genuinely make her smile. But what did she do? She went and kissed another guy that night who looked like him. She loved him but he didn't love her in return. This guy looked like him; intoxicated and drowning in pain her judgement was clouded. She let go of herself and the pain and followed his footsteps. She did what he used to do; cheat.

That night after constant thoughts driving her insane as to why he was the way he was, she let go. She tried to be like him, just to experience what it was he loved about cheating, about betraying people who loved him and unknowingly and unintentionally she ended up hurting you. She didn't mean to. I know people say cheating isn't a mistake but a choice, but are people that are broken to the core, destroyed to the maximum capacity and ruined to the ground really capable of making wise choices? No, right? Neither was she that night, not any other night that her thoughts went back to him. She was trying. She was trying her hardest to make it work with you, not for the sake of forgetting him or moving on from him but because she genuinely liked you and wanted it to work. She just wasn't capable of it at that moment in time. At times it takes to completely lose yourself to find yourself again.

She was sorry she cheated but she never ever meant to hurt you. She never ever wanted to lose you. The day she lost you was the day she lost herself all over again. Not because she lost real love in the form of you, but because she had yet again made another gross mistake as a result of her love. Sorry doesn't make things okay nor does it lessen the pain much but what it does do is give you closure. It helps you move on a little knowing the person who hurt you actually realized their mistake because trust me there are many people that never realize how much they've hurt you... simply because they are under the impression that they are never wrong.

"Please forgive me... I never meant to hurt you"... she said.

When I'm done... I'm done.

There are only so many chances you can give someone... no matter how much you want him or her to be a part of your life.

However, there comes a time when you have to weigh the pros and cons and decide whether this person is actually worth the pain they are constantly causing you, whether their up and down mood swings are worth ruining your day for or whether them always letting you down is actually genuine.

They say if you keep giving people chance over chance, they not only lose respect for you but you in return are allowing them to walk all over you. You're giving them the power to hurt you again, to let you down once again or even to destroy you. You're making them believe that no matter what they do, you'll forgive them.

Not an image you want people to have of you; because that's what people want, they want to walk all over you, they want numerous chances at breaking you, lying to you, making fake promises and then leaving you to pick up the pieces all by yourself.

If you ever make the mistake of taking back someone who has wronged you in any way whether it be betrayal, lies or cheating; don't ever believe that things will change. People never change and if you ever really loved someone you would never hurt them in the first place. You wouldn't lie to them, you wouldn't shout at them in an aggressive manner nor would you break them because the truth is you don't break the people you love.

Being betrayed by a loved one hurts like nothing you've experienced before, but what you and they don't know is that taking them back hurts you more. You're fighting a constant battle with yourself on whether or not you made the right decision or not. The hurt they caused you in the first place never ever goes away, the pain in your chest when it tightens up is a reminder of the agony they gave you that doesn't have a snooze button.

Some people learn the hard way; but once you walk away from someone, don't go back. Once you're done, just be done. Remember there's a huge reason you walked away in the first place. It's tough. It's hard. Leaving your comfort zone will be one of the hardest things you will ever do but one of the best decisions you will make in life as well.

Walk away... be done when you say you're done.

Say it... I want to hear it.

I want to hear what could have happened to possibly change your mind within the blink of an eye. What made you turn away from a lifetime of happiness with the one you claimed to have loved from the deepest depths of your heart that was one filled with love? How did you manage to turn away from the love of your life with such ease? Did your heart not break... even a little? Did you not feel a constant pain in your chest when you turned away from an emotion that allows you to live a little when life gives you many reasons to give up and choose the road that leads to death?

Say it... I want to hear it.

What possibly could have changed your heart and make it go hard and emotionless? How did you manage to forget all the memories that we created, all the nights spent talking about everything and nothing, all the ice creams shared, all the pain halved? Was it that easy? Was it that easy to just walk away?

Say it... I want to hear it.

Who made you God, enough to break a person, so pure and innocent? How could you break someone's belief in love, hope for happiness and shatter his or her dreams of a brighter future? Why make promises you had no intention of keeping? How can you promise someone a lifetime of companionship but then walk away before the journey has even begun? It's funny when a prince charming actually turns out to be a cowardly toad and that's exactly what you were. Scared of commitment and sharing your life with someone you truly loved or at least claimed to have loved.

Say it... I want to hear it.

CHAPTER 6: LIFE AS WE KNOW IT

Change is constant... but that doesn't make it easy.

Change – an act or process as a result of which something becomes different.

Most if not all people resist change, only because they focus on what they have to give up rather than focusing on what they may gain as a result of this change.

I feel change is important in life – it allows us to grow, to adapt, to learn, to gain new experiences and so much more. Think about your life when you were 10 years old and then 20 years old... would you be happy today if your life was the exact same way it used to be at that stage of your life? No right?

Life is never the same... because of constant change. We go through so many transformations in life, in our body, in our relationships, in our jobs, in our education status and every single aspect of our lives.

Relationships change, people come and go and it still baffles me how you can talk to someone every single day for hours on end and then boom, one day it all stops and you don't do that anymore because that person isn't a part of your life. And I am not talking about death; I am talking about people changing like seasons. It can be friends, lovers and even blood. They say you get to know the true face of a human being in times of distress and difficulty. In your darkest times, if you have people that try to light a candle in your life, those are the ones you want by your side in your life forever.

Lovers change way more frequently than the weather in today's society – simply because people are a lot more intolerant now. A 60-year-old couple once said, they've had 40 years of a happy blissful marriage because in their time when there is a problem, they'd fix it, they'd find a solution, they don't leave everything and run away – they face the issues rather than taking the easy way out. No matter what happens, love doesn't change, at least true love doesn't. Not for me anyway.

Our bodies change – people lose weight, people gain weight but they are the same person deep inside. It bothers me when people are judged and seen differently when there is a change in their weight or appearance. Just because I cut off four inches of my hair and look a lot younger, does not mean I am childish now. I have just changed my look. People get bored. It isn't a crime.

As they say don't judge a book by its cover. Don't judge a person by their change in appearance. Judge them by a change in their heart. I don't trust people who claim to love me or be there for me one day but then when I actually need them, they are nowhere to be seen. Be scared of those people whose love changes with the weather or the minute you do something they don't approve of.

Change Management – something I believe not only businesses but human beings should work on as well. I believe even human beings need training on this matter as we are probably the only living things that go through the most changes in life. Businesses these days are going through transformation and restructuring and reorganise their organisations to deal with external change and as a result give their employees the training on change management to deal with it all. Don't we need this training too? So we can better deal with the changes in our lives? So that we don't run away from every problem that we face? So we can deal with people exiting our lives better? So we can deal with losing a job in a positive way rather than looking at it like the end of our lives?

I can't tell you just how much change has gone on in my short life let alone the numerous changes I have been through in the last 12 months. I can't say I dealt with it all like I would have liked to now that I look back but it has definitely given me the training on 'change management' that I guess I needed. It has made me a lot more adaptive to change and I learnt a very valuable lesson – life is all about change and one should always embrace it with a smile.

People in this world.

There are various kinds of people in this world. This world is filled with people.

You can't just categorize them in a good or bad category because people are broader than that.

There are those that are genuinely nice and then there are those that pretend to be nice but are actually being fake. Some people are nice to you because you are rich, some are nice to you because you have something they want and some are nice to you because you can do them favours and they very well know that. For example, at school, girls hang out with you because you are clever and can do their homework or in other cases where you are popular and they want to be seen as your friends.

Then there are those people who are not just bad but vile, they are the one who nearly kill you by giving you a heart attack by depicting the level that they can stoop too. And these people can be anyone, mostly strangers, but can be family members and in worse cases even close friends, mostly those who have called you their brother or sister. Those are the ones to look out for because the way it goes is that they are the ones who will stab you in the back so hard and sharp that you won't even realize what or how or why that happened.

Not everyone you meet is nice and not everyone you meet is bad. The world is filled with different kinds of people. It is human nature to test everyone under the same light after a bad experience or a betrayal but that is not always how it goes. Yes – when someone breaks your trust or in some cases your heart, it is very difficult to trust again or to even want to talk to people in any way, shape or form. But truth is no matter how hard you try, you can't ignore people, you can't just shut yourself off from the world. We have to live in this world and hence, there will be some form of interaction with people – and people of all kinds, good, bad and the ugly.

As very rightly said by Charles M. Schulz, "I love mankind... it's people I can't stand!!"

Truth is don't expect anything from anyone – this way you are saving yourself from disappointments. And also when someone shows you their true colours, believe them right away – don't give them another chance to hurt you or upset you.

In life you'll face many situations where the true colours of people will be revealed to you – take it as a lesson on your chin and learn from it rather than letting those nasty human beings bring you down or dampen your colour and happiness in any way. The truth is it's only you in this world by yourself; the sad reality of life is that you can't really depend on anyone or expect anything from anyone. Be happy within yourself only then will you be able to gain happiness from others or give any in return.

People that say they can't be alone or be without another person surprise me because if you can't be content alone then how can you even be another one's companion. Truth is whether we admit it or not we are all riding solo – we came into this world and we shall depart alone – what we bring in and take with us are memories – memories that we have made on this earth and memories that we gift our loved ones when we come into this world.

People... just good and bad?

I think what amazes me the most in life is people, especially when you learn that there's not just the good and bad type. The types just keep on surprising you. People are selfish, self-absorbed, jealous and spiteful and the worst ones are those that just know how to use you. Thanks to this terrible kind, it makes it so difficult for you to trust and believe in the ones that are actually genuine and sincere with you. But hey... that's just the tragedy of life.

Someone once said there are only two types of people in this world, good and bad. But I don't agree with that. I don't think people that use you for their own benefit, manipulate you, break you and make you lose faith in mankind are bad, they are the worst. You don't want to allow someone like that into your life. Sadly though today we live in a society where it's all about using and abusing people. People will use you and then throw you away like a dirty tissue paper. And these aren't just any random people; they can be anyone from family, to friends to colleagues. You just never know with anyone these days.

There are people who will claim to love you but will control and manipulate you in a way where you completely lose yourself because you have been forced to become someone you are clearly not; just because you feel that you need to be that person to please the one who loves you. But truth is that's not real love. If someone loves you, they should love you for who you are and not for what they want you to be.

Then there's those people who will love the bones off of you, will worship the ground that you walk on – the selfless, genuinely loving kind. These are the ones that you should surround yourself with because these compassionate souls will make your life worth living with their love and sincerity. However, those unfortunate ones out of us that have been unlucky and have experienced life with more monsters than angels, it is difficult for us to actually accept these kind-hearted people when they try to enter our lives.

Though I'm a huge believer of letting the past be in the past and letting go... truth is your past and past experiences will always be a huge part of who you are and nothing can change that. They might not define you today but they will definitely influence your future decisions and that is something that is inevitable, especially if you have been to hell and back in life.

They say good things happen to those who wait, but during this time some go through so much that one would never ever expect to survive or come out of it the same way. But then again, I believe at times when we go through shit in life, it is as though we have been put into a washing machine; twisted, spun around and squeezed out of all the bad water that we had been carrying around like a burden with us – yet, even after going through all that we come out new, bright and much wiser. Though, agreed; the damage done can never be reversed, though I do believe it can be healed and we do heal from experiences... just like we would from bruises. Some might argue that all damages leave a mark; something like a scar but I say that scar is a trophy of what you went through to achieve the success you are enjoying today. There is always another way of looking at a situation.

If you see people that aren't good for your soul and wellbeing, run a mile. We no longer live in a society where we should give monsters second chances; only for them to then double the dose of the poison they inject us with.

The same place...

Yep... the same place... walking past it today... nine years later... still hurt... it brought back all the memories; I never thought it would, after all this time.

I never thought it would take my breath away or make me stop and pause... I had to stop for a second to get my breath back. I still saw us both sitting outside on the steps. Those laughs, the banter, the work, the experience we were gaining at work, we were so young... taking the first step to build our futures. Who would have thought it would ruin mine?

I hope you're okay and happy. I know you miss our friendship and me... but I just couldn't. I couldn't carry on, not after knowing what you had done to me, but now you're doing it to someone else. You can't play with the lives of those who trust you, love you and care about you. It doesn't work like that. I really hope you realize that what you did and are still doing is wrong. They don't deserve that. Sometimes I wish things were different but then again I also believe people come into our lives for a reason – play their part in our movie and leave.

Maybe my part was done in your movie. However, life isn't a movie and just because my part may have ended doesn't mean my care does too. I still wish you all the best. We've been through so much over the last nine years... the ups, the downs, the laughs, the tears and the friendship.

But nothing lasts forever.

Tears – Don't cry over someone who wouldn't cry over you!

Tears – they're a replacement when we're lost for words.

They are our body's way of telling us when our hearts have had enough and cannot take any more pain. At times they flow when we least expect them to, like when we see a stranger on their death bed in a hospital, or a close friend in agony, an aunt crying over her son, a best friend trying on a wedding dress, your mum suffering from an illness or losing love.

And then there are those times when no matter how much you want to cry you can't... you're not sure why not but you just can't. I guess it happens to those who have ran out of tears – perhaps from too much pain, or from pretending to be strong for way too long. It happens... it happens to the best of us. Someone once said don't cry over someone who wouldn't cry for you, but it's funny how life works – we normally cry because of those who would never cry over us. At times, in life it is better to cry it out... especially when you are dealing with unbearable pain, pain that you can't do much about... fact is most of the time we don't have control over this pain.

Everyone is different... some cry it out in front of the world, then there are those that literally can't cry and then those that cry in the dark of the night when no one knows but still have the guts to wake up with a big smile the next morning – one that brightens the lives of others, especially those around them. It's weird, it is these people that feel the most broken and weak but in reality are the strongest people you'll ever know. If you're hurting, cry it all out – you'll definitely feel lighter. And if you can't seem to cry, don't hate yourself, you've just ran out of your yearly supply but will be refilled soon.

I Understand...

Two words... are all it takes. These two words mean a lot when you hear them from someone who actually does understand. And it's difficult when someone close to you doesn't.

What I've learnt though is that not everyone does... no, not everyone understands... in fact no one does, especially those that you expect understanding from.

In life, we can't expect anyone to understand how we feel or what we've gone through. Of course, because how can someone else understand why we don't want to get out of bed on a bright sunny day, or why your friend suddenly doesn't want to meet you despite having had plans or why your eyes have tears in them while all you're doing is sitting in a coffee shop sipping on your coffee.

It takes a kind, caring and compassionate heart to be there, to listen and most importantly to understand.

I wish there was someone who'd understand, someone who'd instantly know when I'm wearing a fake smile that's not reaching my eyes, someone who'd then turn it upside down. There are not many people that can make you smile without an ulterior motive, people that just want to see you happy. There are people out there who'd do anything to see you smile... literally anything. I've been that person for someone I truly loved and cared about. In this selfish world, surprisingly there are people who are selfless, who only care about the happiness of the ones they love and want to see them happy.

Understanding someone's pain is the best gift you can give them... especially to those that you claim to love and care about. It might be a tough job but all it takes is a listening ear, an open mind and a compassionate heart.

Birthdays

There are two great days in a person's life – the day we are born and the day we discover why. Birthdays have always been very special to me – it's just another day, another excuse celebrating life. We should celebrate each day like it's our birthday because truth is life is too short to be taken for granted or to live feeling miserable.

You never know when your time may be up – so celebrate your life yourself before it becomes something people mourn over every year on your death anniversary. Birthdays are so special, from your very first birthday to your sweet 16, that special 21st birthday that makes you an adult or those 30, 40, 50 and 60 milestones. I love birthdays, what's better than being surrounded by your loved ones, big smiles, everyone dancing, lots of yummy cake and thoughtful presents.

I believe that remembering someone's birthday is very special, it says a lot about you as a person and also about your feelings towards that person. I always admire those people that remember my birthday without the aid of any social media. I mean how hard is it to just remember a date? Especially not for those that you love and care about.

And then there are those... whom despite remembering their birthday you can't wish them. Those are the ones that hurt. People that have perhaps walked out of your life or you might have walked out of theirs for whatever reason. What kills me the most is the urge to wish a happy birthday to that one person; whose birthday has always meant the world to me; has meant more to me than my own birthday. God is a witness to how I've waited for that one person to wish me a happy birthday on every one of my birthdays for the last nine years.

Of course, I didn't always get my birthday wish. It's quite normal in life to not get what we really want from the bottom of our hearts.

Here I am thinking about their birthday again... thinking of what I should do... whether I should wish them a happy birthday or just send flowers. I don't know why I feel like this even after so long, despite not getting one on mine. Love isn't always about give and take. True love is and has always been selfless. Birthdays – they always bring a smile to my face now because I've stopped waiting for that one wish.

Scars

'The marks humans leave are too often scars.' 'The wound is the place where the light enters you.' 'I don't want to die without any scars.' It has been said, 'time heals all wounds.' 'Out of suffering have emerged the strongest souls; the most massive characters are seared with scars.'

Every so often we get hurt, scrape our elbow or knee, undergo surgery, damaged tissue and painful pregnancy. These scars however result in just temporary pain or in some cases slight or no pain at all. However, the scars that are given to us by other humans are the ones that hurt the most and often kill us... resulting not in death but something more damaging, a life lived waiting for death.

Often the scars given to us by humans are the ones that leave us completely broken in more pieces than we actually knew we were made of... it is rather unbelievable how that happens. Humans have the two most powerful things that God has given us the ability to do, which allow them to hurt other people and scar them for life... words and actions that are done without any thought behind it.

Whether it's heartbreak through lies and cheating, deceit through a family member or loved one or a traumatizing experience thanks to a stranger who couldn't handle their drink or drugs and lost their minds. Humans are the only ones who have the power to cause those scars not only on our bodies but also especially on our hearts. The scars on our bodies might fade one day, or shall we say with time, but the scars that our loved ones leave on our hearts and especially on our souls are so deep and life threatening that they can often lead us to our death or should we say to lives that we live in melancholia. I too have been living with a scar on my heart and recently another one on my soul... and I can't express in words just how much that hurts, it absolutely kills... bit by bit... one day at a time.

But on the positive note, there are many just like me who wear their scars more beautifully than those who wear diamonds around their neck. Being scarred for life does do a lot of damage to one's heart and mind, their ability to think rationally and logically. However, it also teaches us a lot, not only about life and people and how we should carry ourselves or rather save ourselves from such human beings... but most of all it teaches us so much about ourselves... how strong we are... and how much more stronger we can be.

Accidents happen... they happen all the time

Life is a gamble. You can get hurt, people die in plane crashes, lose their arms and legs in car accidents and some even lose their lives. Same with fighters: some die, some get hurt, some go on. You just don't let yourself believe it will happen to you. An accident is an unfortunate incident that happens unexpectedly and unintentionally, typically resulting in an injury, damage or at times death.

We hear of road accidents that cause chaos in our life when we're trying to get home; some worse than others; some with reparable damage, but some that end in someone dying. Then there are accidents that happen in the bedroom, which cause an unexpected birth of a new life that changes yours forever. Accidents can happen at any time, accidents happen at work, on the road, slip or trip accidents and some even in places such as hospitals due to medical negligence.

Accidents in life that are life-threatening can be quite traumatising, injurious to health as well as so powerful that they can place a person in a complete state of shock. Road accidents and those due to medical negligence are the ones that are life-threatening and can not only cause death, but also leave people mentally and physically paralysed.

Some accidents can be prevented but others are just unfortunate events. Having recently been in an accident that nearly killed me made me realize that life is way too short to live it with regrets or holding grudges. It made me realize that being organised and planning ahead doesn't mean anything because life is way too unpredictable and we aren't even promised a tomorrow let alone a whole life ahead. Then there are those accidents that can be called a pleasant surprise, accidents of when someone gets pregnant unexpectedly or those when you meet someone coincidentally.

It could almost be argued that just like death and bad luck, happiness comes into our lives accidentally as well. Sometimes it sneaks in through windows that we didn't even realize we left open. But no matter what accident you experience or go through in life... the bitter truth of life is that is goes on... the clock never stops ticking and hence, you need to do the same. Keep moving forward, it is tough to pick yourself up when you've been through something terrible but you have no other choice. It's better to let go of that negative experience than to let go of your life.

Memory Loss

Memory loss, also known as amnesia, happens when a person loses the ability to remember information and events they would normally be able to recall. People that suffer from memory loss/amnesia due to unfortunate events or an unlucky incident experience the disappearance of most if not all of the memories that were stored in their brain for a long period of time and in some cases most of their life. Can you imagine waking up one day and not being able to remember who your loved ones are? Not being able to recognize your other half? Your children? What you do for a living? Basically your entire identity.

I struggle to even imagine how people actually going through this condition day in day out and most of all, the loved ones of the ones suffering from amnesia cope. How tough must it be when your own father can't remember the fact that you are his child, he can't remember how much he loves you and how he has looked after you and brought you up to be the successful individual you are today. How do you look at someone you love and make them believe that you are who you say you are? How do you tell your grandmother that their child that they have asked you to call to the hospital bed has died some 10 years ago? How do you look at your mother and tell her that you are their only child when she actually thinks you're some horrible girl who took her husband away from her? How do you look at your husband with tears in your eyes after a car crash that he has survived which you are pleased about – but then he looks at you with just questions of your identity in his eyes?

How do you deal with something like that? We say it so easily – I wish I could forget this or forget that and in most cases, I wish I could forget you. That is the most common one that is wished for. There are moments in life where we really pray and hope that we could forget something terrible that has happened in our lives, simply to forget the pain associated with that incident, then there are those people that we try our hardest to forget perhaps because they have broken our hearts or us as individuals. There are also those horrible humans beings that have hurt us or caused us harm.

But truth is forgetting isn't in our power – if one day we suffer from amnesia, we will forget most of what we don't want to forget, but whilst we can't forget what we deeply do and are trying to forget. It is important that we do remember no matter how much we want to forget; we make sure that we still remember. It is vital to remember how you were wronged, betrayed and cheated by someone, be it a close friend, your own blood family or a lover because once we forget we set up ourselves for disaster. It is vital we remember every experience we have been through in the sense that we don't allow ourselves to go through something that hurt us ever again.

When we've had enough of a pain that we have been dealing with for as long as we can remember... sometimes we wish we could just erase that memory from our brain and heart so that in return the melancholy would end but that doesn't happen. They say what doesn't kill you makes you stronger, living with what may feel like a never ending pain feels much easier to deal with than to not remember who you are, who your loved ones are and what life you live.

So remember while you still can, cherish the joyous memories, learn from the painful ones and keep on creating new one because in the end memories will be all that you are left with.

What is Mental Health?

Mental health – a very sensitive topic to talk about or discuss for most. Mental health refers to our psychological, emotional and social wellbeing which as a result has an impact on how we think, how we feel and how we act. It is also a condition that helps determine how we handle stress, how we relate to those around us along with the life choices we make that have a huge impact not only on our life but also a reverse effect on our mental well-being. Mental health is an important aspect of our lives from childhood and adolescence right through to adulthood.

If ever in life you experience mental health problems, this has a significant impact on your thinking, mood and mainly your behaviour not just towards others, but mainly about yourself. You almost start seeing yourself in a completely different light, there are some that blame themselves for things that aren't and never were their fault; whereas some start putting the entire blame on others.

The fact is one in four people of the world's population will experience mental health problems in any given year and the truth also is that we *ALL* work with at least one person who is suffering from such disorders. One of the most common mental health problems includes mixed anxiety and depression, which can often lead to panic attacks.

These can either be genetic or a result of an experience that an individual has been through. Mental health changes a person forever; you're not the same person anymore as you were before any of it. The drugs that you are prescribed mess with your brain, with your ability to do, say and react to normal everyday things. It is not something people expect to have to deal with or experience; once again it is a very inevitable condition. The struggle is hard or to some may seem unbearable and rather helpless. It is difficult when you don't know why you're feeling a certain way, or why you did what you did last night, whether it was cutting your wrist or telling your best friend to bugger off from your life, why you can't eat like a human being anymore, why you can't seem to do anything right anymore or perhaps that is just how you feel.

Suffering from mental health issues is one thing and dealing with them is another. Twenty per cent of the world's population deal with psychological issues or shall suffer and sadly some are even suffering alone in silence. Even though we live in a modern society, unfortunately mental health is still an issue that is seen as a taboo, the same way sex before marriage was seen in the olden days. However, having sex outside of wedlock is a choice for most whereas being diagnosed with a mental condition isn't in our power. Hence, many suffer in silence or even if those around them know, they aren't very helpful. So how are you meant to help yourself if there is only negativity and discrimination around you? Be kind to everyone you meet, no matter if they have mental health issues or not, because truth is every single one of us is fighting a battle deep down that you know nothing about. Be compassionate, there are plenty of heartless people in this world so let's try and make this world a better place to live in.

Running away...

We are all running away from something that is bothering us deep inside, something that we constantly struggle to come to terms with, a problem we just don't want to face, a challenge that seems impossible. But does that help? Does running away from what is breaking you from within your soul and everything in you make things easier? Does it make the problem go away? Does it automatically make the problem disappear when you come back? No it doesn't.

The truth is, running away is a race you will never win. You know why? Because anyone can run away, it's super easy. Facing problems and walking through them, that is what makes you strong. There's this story of a girl who always ran away from her problems because that is how she dealt with life or rather was forced to. Her parents had a disastrous marriage where her father used to beat and abuse her mother. As a child and their only child she would stay away from home, escape in the garden or the poolside. She loved singing so she would take her guitar and always run away to the furthest part of their huge house and sing to drown out the fighting noises of her parents.

She always questioned her mother for staying with a man who'd verbally and physically abuse her and she'd always reply that it was because the generation that she was from would stick with a marriage because they did not believe in divorce. She then met this mister nice guy at college who adored her and worshipped the ground she walked on... there were feelings there but as soon as she realized she liked him she took a step back and quit college. After all, she had only ever learned to escape, to run away and that is exactly what she did when she met love.

That boy was heartbroken when she quit college to go and marry someone she didn't love. However, they met again two years later because no matter how hard we try to run away, we don't know what fate has in store for us. She was now a divorcee but because he truly loved her, he couldn't care less about her status but of course his mother did, especially when she found out that she has a past of leaving things and running away from problems. She warned her to stay away from her son.

And of course as always she left him without saying goodbye with a note saying she wasn't good for him and hence, she was leaving and asked him not to look for her. But how could he abide by that? He truly loved her; the kind of love that takes your breath away, the kind of love that if lost can take your smile away along with your will to live. Rather than running away, what she should have done was confronted him about his feelings and whether or not he cared about her status of a divorcee.

Running away doesn't get you far in life. Trust me. I've tried and tested it. Deal with your problems, because the truth is no matter how far you go, it'll never leave you, it'll always be there in the back of your mind, in the deepest corners of your heart and one day will appear right in front of you; breaking you all over again. Don't give it that power. Deal with your problems, don't run away. Face them. Be strong. Solve the problems and close the chapter.

CHAPTER 7: THAT ONE PERSON

Who Are You... ?

Where have you come from? And why?

What do you want from me? Have you come to hurt me? Destroy me? Break me?

If yes, please don't bother. I have been through all that already.

Why are you being so nice? What is your ulterior motive? What is it that you want from me?

Surreal. Surreal is the word I would use for you. Not sweet. Not nice. Not genuine. Simply surreal. You don't seem real to me. How can you be so personable, so pleasant, so likeable and so good-natured? Are you even human?

Why are you so much like me? They say you are the male version of me? But why do I find that so hard to believe? I've never met anyone like you... someone so sincere, so honest and so genuine. Hence, I keep saying you seem so surreal. You're not selfish like he was, you actually care about my wellbeing unlike him, you pray to God for my long life, whereas he nearly killed me.

My face without a smile hurts you whereas he only decorated my eyes with an ocean of tears. You've promised never to make me cry and always want to see me smile. But why is it that since him I've forgotten how to smile? Why is it that I've cried so much thanks to him that I don't have any more tears left?

Why does my smile matter so much to you? Why is it that you want to live your life with me the exact same way I've always wanted to live mine with him? Why is it that your feelings seem purer than anything I have ever felt before? And why is it my heart doesn't feel the same? Why is it I feel numb? Feel heartless? Emotionless as some may say?

I guess time will tell... I should just leave all this to time because right now... I don't know who you are...!

Kaputt

Why did you do this? Why didn't you tell me that you were going to do this? I never asked you to come into my life and cause mayhem. Some people come into our lives disguised as angels and that is exactly what you were. But little did I know that an angel can cause such destruction.

I still remember the very day; those sparkling eyes... that cute yet cheeky smile... those mesmerizing lips... and what got me the most... as stupid as it sounds... your funny anime T-shirt. I hate that T-shirt now because if it weren't for that I would have never spoken to you or given you a second glance. It was cheeky of me to ask when you'd do laundry next just so I could steal that T-shirt from you; that's where it all began right? I wonder why I did that... I just found it really cute... especially the colour too. Bright blue... a happy blue.

We were walking in a group yet separate... do you remember when it was just the two of us sitting on the stairs and you opened up to me? I didn't expect that... I just asked a general question but I guess you needed someone to offload on anyone anyway... I'm glad I could be there for you. Not going to lie I didn't expect you to cry on my shoulder for someone else. Though it was nice being there for you – but you really made me feel like a heartless soul. Watching you cry... I wished I could too. Letting it all out helps so much and knowing that I still couldn't, hurt. Ran out of tears I guess.

Since then I guess we had an invisible bond, two people with similar experiences, similar melancholia, similar pains and I guess similar hearts that were just looking for some healing. I'm glad I was your medicine, the one that healed you, gave you back your smile, made you love again and brought you back to life. What did you do? And why? I still don't understand why you did what you did. What was my fault after all? What did I do so wrong that you had to break me so brutally?

I can never get over what you did... you not only broke me but destroyed my soul – not sure if it'll ever be the same again. But what's even more despairing is that you don't even think you did anything wrong. Nearly killing someone is wrong. Putting your hands on someone is wrong. In any religion. In any country. In any context. There is no justification for it. I still ask myself why you did what you did. Why did you break me?

Today... just once

Nothing special about today. Just that I feel it a lot more. I can feel the pain in my chest, the lump in my throat and the ache in my heart. I wish you could understand. I wish I could tell you. I wish you would listen. Anyone reading this might think only a genie can help me with all these wishes I keep stating.

But what do I do? I can't seem to let go. I can't seem to get over the pain. The memories, the laughs, the shared pizzas, the scary movies, the long walks, the unbelievably amazing trips away... and most of all... us.

I wish you were here. How do I tell you that I need you? They say at times the one who has caused you the immense pain is the only one that can take it away... I need you to take it away.

I look up at the sky most nights... hoping for answers... asking God why He brought you in my life... made you such a huge part of my life when He didn't plan on letting you be a part of it. Why?

I don't let people get close because I know they always leave... but you said you never would. You'd always be there.

Even when you were thousands of miles away. You were still there... bugging me, annoying me with your silly little questions and then making me smile with your cuteness and stupidity.

You became my best friend... my day wouldn't start without your 'Good Morning' or end without your nonsense jokes. I miss that... I miss calling you an idiot... I miss telling you off for doing stupid things and not listening to my sensible advice. I miss our shenanigans... I miss that hug from my best friend that would make everything okay in just a second.

I always wonder why He separated you from me. I wish He hadn't brought you into my life if this friendship wasn't meant to last. Because now I feel lost without you. I wish you could come back... just once.

Tu me manques

It's weird... people say time heals all wounds... but does it though? I've never believed in this saying. I really don't think time heals anything. I think what it does though is, teach us how to live with the unbearable pain.

Tu me manques... is how the French say 'I Miss You', but the French don't say that, because the direct translation is that 'you are missing from me'. After all there's a reason why they're known as the most romantic lovers – we can just see that from the way they express their longing for someone.

And I guess that is exactly what I am trying to say to you or rather express to you... my longing for you... how my heart has been and still is longing for you and in a way always has. I really miss you... there's not a single second in the day when you're not on my mind... where I don't think about you... think about the past... the time we spent together... the way I felt when I was with you... the way you made me feel when you looked at me... the way I felt when all I did was watch you watching me. I want all that back... tu me manques... you're missing from me.

I know I made mistakes, big ones, stupid ones, hurtful ones, but not a single one was to hurt you... I loved you damn it...

really, really loved you. I always wished you'd see that... in my eyes; that sparkled when they looked at you, on my face that would light up seeing your smile; my lips that wouldn't stop smiling whilst admiring you; the time I spent with you... that became so invaluable just by your presence; the food that tasted so much better than it was, simply because it was made for you; me looking at the reflection of myself in the mirror, that looked beautiful only because you made me look beautiful. I loved you... with all my heart; and I always hoped then and still do that everything I did for you showed you that.

Our love was beautiful, unreal and pure... a love that I guess wasn't meant to be, but then why is it that it is still alive? Why is it that despite all odds, our love is still growing, why is it that it hasn't died? Why? What has this surreal love got in store for the both of us? They say people outgrow each other, many marriages end in a divorce because of this very reason then why is it that hasn't been the case with us? Why? Surely we've had many occasions where our love could have lost but it hasn't... why? We both know we tried... to forget each other, to move on, to stop loving each other and here we are... falling in love again, all over again or maybe we never stopped. I don't think I did, because I still do... maybe even more than before.

But no matter how much I love you, the truth of the matter is that... tu me manques... you're missing from me.

Not everyone you lose is a loss

While we acknowledge the fact that not everyone who enters our lives will stay for quite some time, losing someone isn't at all times a loss. I believe life is like a movie, where God is the director and the people who come and go are the characters in our movie. And truth is not everyone is meant to stay for the whole movie and that is exactly why, not everyone who walks into our lives, is meant to stay.

It's funny when we say that loss of a loved one kills us because the truth is when we lose someone due to death we know that they're never coming back, but when we lose someone to life that's when it hurts and kills you inside, not just on the day that you lose them but every single day after that... it's a slow death inside.

But the bitter truth of life also is that not everyone you lose in life is a loss; sometimes you're gaining space that that person had been occupying when they really didn't deserve it. It could be a family member, yes believe it or not blood can be dirty too, a friend – funny when it is a best friend who you considered a sister and last but not least, a lover – believe it or not lovers can come and go too.

We get members of our family that are pure evil and will only use you for selfish reasons, whether it be money, support or your kids. It is unbelievable how your blood can be like that and it hurts at first and your mind and heart are not willing to believe it, but when the reality hits that's when you realize that you are actually better off without them. I mean why deal with people just because they are your family but are selfish, cunning and sly towards you and your family. What value are they adding to your life or home exactly? None, hence you're better off without them. Life is too short to be dealing with such people, trust me, it doesn't make a different if they are blood or not, your life won't be prolonged just because they are your family.

Life doesn't stop for anyone, the sooner some people realize that the better. As I say... good riddance. What I've seen and experienced is that God replaces those evil so called family members with genuine friends who actually act like a family and eventually become your family and you stop filling the void of those who were supposed to be blood. What hurts the most though is when friends betray you and as a result you lose them... but truth also is that not every so-called friend you lose is a loss. It is wise to choose the right friends because they become your family as well as being such a huge part of your life, and when they've become exactly that... it's hard to deal with a betrayal from them. It can literally kill you. But then it could also be said that that's when you realize their true friendship, their loyalty towards you and most importantly their true colours.

Some friends are only there for you when it suits them or is convenient for them and not when you need them the most... so... are they even true friends? There are also those ones who can't see you succeed or climb up the ladder, why? Simply because they couldn't. What has that got to do with you? Or your friendship but unfortunately you do get people under the whole 'best friend' mask who can't be happy for you just because they think their life sucks... and hence, will do anything to ruin yours.

Those aren't your friends, those are just people who pretend to be your friends because the truth is anyone who is genuine to you will always and I mean it, always be there for you no matter what is going on in their own life and will be happy for you when you succeed and pick you up when things go downhill. Not someone who will resent you for going away to fulfil your dreams and career aspirations. It's an absolute joke. And hence, losing such people isn't exactly a loss. Sometimes it takes losing someone to actually realize their worth and value in your life. Not everyone deserves a place in your life. If they don't add value to you or your life and only destroy your inner peace – let them go! Toodles!

A beautiful day

Every day spent with love is a beautiful day but there was something special about that day... it was a beautiful sunny day. As always we woke up all cuddled up in each other's arms... until you started pestering me for breakfast; you never could control hunger... especially on the weekends. I made you yummy waffles that day remember? With special Kit Kat melted on them. And once you got your breakfast in bed...

I could breathe. You really were like a baby... non-stop tantrums until you were fed... and once you were fed... my baby was nice and calm and ready to play.

After breakfast we went for a shower... you always did love my gorgeous smelling scented candles that I liked keeping in the bath. It's funny, it's the little things in life that we miss, that make us smile and want to go back... just to relive it one more time... just one last time. We went to the park that afternoon, the one near the beautiful bridge, the one you knew I loved. Walking around hand in hand... with love in our eyes... we couldn't have asked for anything more. After all it was such a beautiful day... bright and sunny... and two people in love.

I would do anything to go back to that day... to spend that whole day with you again... hand in hand... I still remember... it was so cold... and I just wanted to be in your arms, cuddled up and all warm. Then again there's been so many beautiful and happy memories that we've had that I would give anything to relive. Just to see you smile again... I'd make that cute funny face all day long if it meant I could see you smile again. Believe it or not your smile meant everything to me. I really do wish I could see it again... just this once.

Until it turned upside down and it was close to dinnertime and my baby was hungry again... I mean how? Like how? We had just had three scoops of yummy ice cream –most of it which you had... as always. After all my baby was always hungry, like all the time. Hungry, angry and sleepy.

We then went to the square and had your favourite pizza! Honestly speaking I've never had so much pizza in my entire life, as much as I had whilst I was with you. You almost reintroduced pizza back into my life. I miss our pizza weekends, I can't believe just how much you loved pizza – you loved it more than you ever loved me. I guess I became your pizza partner – our weekends with us in each other's arms, pizza, Pepsi, our love and a movie. That's all we ever needed. We didn't need to go to a fancy restaurant every week, or go to the cinema or go for fun activities because we didn't need any of that. We both were more than enough for each other.

After dinner we went into my favourite shop and I tried on a 300 quid dress! Remember? You made me into a model for a while – so many pictures, so many poses and most of all so many memories. It was so much fun – we were happy doing nothing. It was a beautiful day, all the laughs, my tears near the bridge when I realized just how much I'd miss you when you'd leave, the ice cream that wasn't equally shared, the pizza, the cuddles, the endless photographs, the love... and *US* – two crazy people crazily in love.

I Miss You – Part 2

For some reason... I've been missing you a lot these past few days to the point where it's hurting me physically... I've been feeling this sharp pain in my chest and even in my heart... the ache takes my breath away. But last night it got worse... I could barely breathe... the sharp pains in my chest were making it very difficult for me to breathe or shall I say live. I missed you terribly... I wanted to talk to you... to call you... just to hear your voice... so this heart that belongs to you... that beats for you would just take a breath and calm down. But... I couldn't. I knew you wouldn't answer the phone or more importantly care... care about how I was feeling... after all you do blame me for my hearts condition. You think I've caused my broken heart this pain but I haven't. I mean what human being in their right mind would cause themselves this melancholy or this agony that appears to be a slow death?

Just as any relationship, we had our ups and downs, our laughs and tears, our fights and making up sessions, our love, anger but most of all we had each other, we had *US* and I guess that's what hurts the most... not having you. You seem to have gone so far away from me... I know long distance relationships are hard but with us it was more a distance between us and our hearts than the geographical distance. I wish I had never let you go... had trapped you in my arms like I would do most mornings when you would try to leave for work and I'd wrap my legs around you and say, "No, no, no... " So mad I was... jealous of your old boss and blaming her of taking you away from me in the mornings.

Such cute memories.

I know we had a lot of ups and downs, we had both hurt each other by doing things that were wrong, we eventually did forgive as well, and surprisingly still love each other despite everything that we had been through. If I'm honest, I wish we didn't, I wish I didn't still love you with all my heart... I wish this pain would go away... I wish you hadn't missed me all this while and I wish I hadn't blacked out while missing you so much that my heart stopped working.

I do wonder what He had planned for us, I often look up to the sky and ask Him, as to why he brought us together? Why did He make us fall in love when I was so adamant that I never would? Why did He make us care so much for each other? Why did we forgive mistakes we never would for another? And most of all why do our hearts still beat for each other even after all this time? They say you're getting bad when your mind and body don't want to get out of bed anymore... I thought I was getting bad... but truth is I'm getting worse... I fall asleep... wishing to never wake up again so I don't have to bear this life threatening pain. Still patiently waiting for the days I don't miss you anymore...

Why... why do I still care?

Why is it that we never stop caring even when the other person does? Why do we still miss them every single day of our lives when it seems like they've clearly forgotten us? I don't get why? Why does it matter to me so much? Why does it feel like I've lost a part of me?

It's strange how you can speak to someone every moment of every day, they become a part of your everyday life, talking to them for hours on end becomes a part of your routine and then there comes a point in life where you've not spoken to them for months let alone hours or days. You go from friends/lovers with memories that are worth a lifetime to strangers who have nothing to say to each other anymore but share the same memories. I struggle to understand why I still care about you so much, and not just about you as what you meant to me, but about your health, about how you're doing without me, about your career because I know how worried you were. My heart still skips a beat every time I miss you, every time I hear our favourite songs, every time I wear one of your T–shirts, every time something reminds me of you... my heart just... it aches... it longs for you and I don't understand why. It is my heart and I am the one who doesn't have any control over it.

Throughout life and the people that have come and gone, I have learnt one thing for sure that no one is permanent in our lives. Everyone in our life has a role to play, a film can personify life, where we are the protagonists and people around us are our supporting characters and not all of them are meant to stay. Someone once said to me people either come into your life as a blessing or as a lesson. Blessings are the ones that you want to keep and hold on tight to. These are the ones that will be by your side no matter what, they'll motivate and encourage you in life and be by your side during not only the happy but sad times as well. And those are your real gems.

Whereas the ones that come as lessons are the ones you want to vary of because even though you only learn from lessons, however, some lessons can not only teach you a hard fact in life but also destroy you as a person, emotionally and mentally. Though on the plus side, when we meet shit people and they put us through hell, they do make us stronger and wiser in our judgment of people in life. So not all is wasted but yes it does still hurt.

No matter what happened between us, I still care about you and miss you deeply, you were a huge part of my life and in some way brought me back to life when you came into it, as at that point I was at a stage in life where I was going downhill. And even though you helped me back up... you did break me on the way up too. There are many things we both wished hadn't happened between us but they did and I guess everything happens for a reason. I know you don't believe me when I say I care, but truth is I do and I won't tell you anymore because there's just no point... but I do and in all honesty I wish I didn't... you know why? Because it hurts...

In the midst of everything there's still that...

They say some pains never leave you... and this one is exactly that. No matter what you do... you always feel it deep inside your heart. Making you ache... making you stop abruptly while walking; either to work or home or while shopping. That sharp pain that shakes your soul in the midst of everything and you seem to zone out... unsure of what to do next, you forget what you were doing in that moment; you become completely oblivious of your surroundings.

Why is it that no matter what happens in life, whether happy or sad moments, you are always there? Why won't you leave me alone? Even one's own shadow leaves us in darkness... but you; you seem to get more close to me in the darkness of my pain, my mistakes, my guilt, my remorse and most of all my heart – that's filled with all these emotions.

They say time heals all... why won't time heal you? You almost seem like cancer but with cancer there is some form of temporary cure to cancer, there is chemotherapy, you can cut out a piece of the cancer out of your body... how do I cut you out of me? How do I cut you out of my heart? How do I separate you from my heartbeats? How do I stop thinking about you? How do I stop feeling the pain? How do I stop living this melancholy; like how?

I wish I could cut you out of me and just breathe normally again, live fearlessly again, love freely again and most of all feel alive again. In the midst of everything there's still... you. I wish you would go away and leave me alone... and if you can't just kill me... end it... because truth is I can't take it anymore.

I just can't.

Is he happy?

And he'll be angry. He'll call her a few names and tell anyone who will listen that she turned out to be this and she turned out to be that. But he will always very conveniently forget to mention all of the real life shit that he did to her, and just how long she took it and even tried to make excuses for it, before she turned and became this and that. But you've got to understand that he is a coward; and that's just the type of shit that cowards do.

He still thinks about her and will look at their pictures together when he's alone in his room; first thing in the morning or just before bed, or on his way to work or while lying on the couch whilst pretending to watch TV. But he will not use the same phone to call her and tell her just how much he misses her and wished he could just talk to her. It kills him when he thinks about her because of the intensity with which his heart misses her voice, his arms miss her touch, his eyes miss her beautiful face and most of all his soul misses his other half. Despite the strength of his longing for her, he will always let his ego win; he will always give power to his anger before his love or what his heart is asking him to do.

He goes out every weekend, partying, drinking himself under the table; pretending that he's happy and showing the world that she doesn't matter to him anymore but when he gets a moment to stop at the club that is filled with people; all he can think of is her, the way she smiled, the way she danced and moved her hips, which drove him crazy, the way she let herself go in his arms at a club... that feeling that despite the hundreds of people at the club, she had chosen his arms to be in – but then he'll remember that she isn't in his arms anymore; he'll remember that she left him without thinking of why, he'll remember all the wrong he thinks she did and within the blink of an eye all that love will be taken over by anger... such extreme vexation that will cloud his eyes and make him almost blind to the pure love and happiness he felt not even a minute ago.

E for ego, I say is the villain in every love; mostly in men as they call it male ego – I don't understand how they let their ego get in the way of the one they truly love, the one girl who made them feel emotions they had never felt before, the one girl they'd do anything for, the one girl they loved like no other – the one girl who they knew from the very second they set their eyes on her that she was 'The One'.

How can you so easily let go of 'The One'? Like how? This life is too short to let your ego take over you and your decisions and cause you to lose the one you love.

He very well knows he won't find any other like her – because there isn't. She was unique, crazy, funny in her own way, cute with the little things she did, compassionate, adorable and most importantly a true lover. You don't always get all these qualities in one person but he was lucky enough to be exactly like – someone who had someone who loved them despite their flaws. But yet he let her go – not because he didn't love her but because he didn't know how to express that love.

Love is a strong emotion – one that is best only expressed and not exercised. Love is being caring and considerate for another and not exercising your power and control over the one you claim to love. Love doesn't teach to abuse or ridicule the one you love if they don't listen to you. Love is trying to solve problems and misunderstandings by listening and consulting with one another. Love isn't delegation or aggression, love is sensitivity and compassion.

Is he happy? I don't know. If not talking to her means he is happy than maybe he is. If thinking all bad things about her means he is happy than maybe he is. If searching for her in every girl he comes across means he is happy than maybe he is. If sleeping with another girl just to get revenge over her means he is happy than maybe he is. If not believing her love that he very well knows he felt every moment that he was with her, means he is happy than maybe he is.

But I still question it – is he happy?

His Love...

His love is deep, his love is wide, it is furious.

His love is fierce, his love is strong, it is forever. She was his everything, his smile, his laughter, his happiness, his blessing in disguise, his success, his courage but most of all his love.

He fell in love with her the minute he saw her and they spoke... though it was quite a coincidental meeting, there were sparks and whether or not they accepted it, they both felt them somewhere deep down. She cared about him in an unintentional and unknowing way even though this was the first time they had met. And he knew there was something special about her, the way she spoke, the way she cared for him and showed him compassion.

She wasn't like any other girl, at least not to him, there was something quite intriguing and attractive about her that led him to walk on a path that led to a beautiful destination, which was her. Before he knew it he had fallen deeply in love with her, after all she was this beautiful person inside and out and the most unique characteristic she had was her selflessness, which he hated most of the time but it is that which got him to fall in love with her. He was amazed at how someone can be so selfless, because that is the only reason he felt he could share one of his biggest pains with her on the very first day that he met her. And he knew that wasn't normal. They both didn't sleep a wink that night... for different reasons; him because she had lit a fire inside him, and her because she was feeling sorry for him and the melancholy his heart was in, because she had been there, she had been over qualified in the heartbreak department of which he was a new member. She felt pain for him because she knew how bad it hurts, how broken you feel and how impossible it seems to move on from something that has changed you completely

But little did she know, his love was true and deep and was growing for her every minute they spent together. He had started caring for her not only because he had started loving her but also because he knew that this selfless being cared and looked after the whole world but herself, she'd put her family and friends before herself and that is not something which was common in todays' world. But that exactly was her USP, she was this independent, strong young woman who didn't need anyone, she was fine by herself or so she made herself believe. But truth is she did need looking after, she needed someone to care for her how she did for everyone else. And that is exactly what he did.

His love for her made him crazy, he'd reprimand her for not looking after herself and would force-feed her when she'd skip meals. He wanted her to get a good night's sleep and get plenty of rest only because he loved her. But what he didn't know was that love can't be controlled or directed in a certain way. He might have appeared controlling and possessive but it was only because he had an abundance of love to give to someone who had shut herself away from this incredible emotion called – love.

His love was larger than the ocean because it not only was tender, endearing but most importantly forgiving. And that is something that is important in every relationship. No two people are perfect, no one love is perfect and hence, we must learn to forgive, we must learn to look past mistakes and flaws. People come and go from your life but true love never leaves you, that person whom you've loved to the moon and back may not be in your life anymore, but the truth is if you truly loved them you always will. Because truth of the matter is that 'You never stop loving someone, either you never did or you always will'. And his love, even today only grows. He still loves her... and always will.

Deep inside...

No one really knows how you're feeling deep inside. Each one of us wanted something or in some cases someone deeply, but it never worked out. Whether this was a particular thing, a place where you wanted to go, that expensive handbag that you wanted but couldn't have or that one person who meant everything to you but you never ended up with.

You don't always get what you want... and sometimes you get way more than you expected or wanted – and this isn't always good.

Sometimes we get a lot more pay than we ever expected in an existing role or the love we get from your in-laws that you never actually got from your own family. On the other hand, you get way more than you ever wanted in some cases – you only wanted love but got abuse and violence in a relationship that was your life. You wanted love and respect from your partner but only got someone who used and abused you. Life doesn't always work out the way we want it to. We don't always get what we want from the deepest depths of our heart but no one knows.

You'll still see that guy going on with his life and his new job who lost over two billion pounds in a business he set up after he graduated, you'll still see that girl who got physically abused by the one guy she truly ever loved, that mother who still regrets staying with her husband just for the safety of her children, the frail old woman living up the street who misses her children every moment of every day, but cannot do anything about it.

Deep inside we are all experiencing some form of pain that only we can feel, that only we are dealing with – a pain that doesn't let us live, a pain that doesn't let us feel, a pain that doesn't let us feel happiness.

We are all fighting a battle deep inside, whether that is within ourselves, with our demons and the ghosts from our pasts or with a wound someone else has caused us. There is always something deep inside that no one else is aware of – something that kills us every single second of every single day. Something we are all trying too hard to get past but haven't quite got there yet. But we will, one day it won't feel this bad. One day the pain will feel bearable. One day you won't be suffering alone. One day you'll be able to look back on the wounds and smile back knowing that you survived and have the scars to show for it.

Everyone is fighting a battle deep inside. Everyone has a pain deep inside them. Everyone has a wound deep inside. Everyone has a different story and only they know because it is their wound, their grief and their battle to deal with.

If you can't help them, at least don't make it worse for them. Always – be kind!

Kindness always has a way of coming back to you in the form of a blessing.

Closure

It's very important to have closure in any relationship that ends – from a romantic relationship to a friendship. You should always have a sense of clarity at the end and know why it began and why it ended. You need that in your life to move cleanly into your next phase. Closure – only happens right after you accept that letting go and moving on is more important than projecting a fantasy of how the relationship could have been. Not everything in life is meant to be, not every couple is meant to be; some people just come into your life to teach you a lesson or as a blessing. As clichéd as it may sound, everything in your life happens for a reason. As they also say what doesn't kill you makes you stronger. Life is full of twists and turns, the good and the bad, the ups and the downs; the darkness and the days with rainbows.

When something bad happens; yes it may break you or even destroy you but eventually it will make you stronger in the long run. Once you close that door, once you decide you want to move on, let go... accept it for what it is when you gain closure. There are many times in life when you don't get closure, when you don't get the answers to the million questions you may have. Why did that happen? Why did he leave? Why did she cheat? Why did my parent leave me? Why did I choose him/her? Why did that job not work out? Why did that relationship not work out?

Not every chapter that you start is meant to turn into a book.

CHAPTER 8: DEATH

Life and Death

Life asked Death...
"Why Do People Love Me But Hate You?"
Death responded...
"Because You Are A Beautiful Lie And I Am A Painful Truth".
We all see death as the end of life but that isn't what death is... life doesn't have an end... life is a journey which just appears to have different stages and phases and death is just one of them. It isn't the end of life but a part of it. There are many people that are fearful of death and I don't understand why because death isn't something that scares me, in fact it is something I have always known to embrace with both arms as one would a loved one. Death isn't the end of a life but just a part of it. Death is more the end of a chapter in one's life. Most poets have called death – a silent peaceful sleep. And that's exactly what it is.

We all will die one day but some have to leave before others and it is not a choice that we always make but more what God has chosen for us and we must accept. When death comes, it is as if our time on this earth and in this life has come to an end. Some of us can argue what about the children who lost their life before it even began? But truth is they had fulfilled their purpose for this life that they had been given and hence they were called by God.

We were created and sent on this earth by God, He is the one who gave us this life and to Him shall we return. Most people see death as a painful loss, but that's not what it is, death is a peaceful deep sleep that lasts longer than the one we take every day, it is a place filled with tranquillity where no pain, drama or difficulties can reach you. It is finally the place we search for all our lives where we at last feel at peace. The fear of death follows from the fear of life. A man who lives fully is prepared to die at any time.

Would it have mattered... does death even matter?

Having come back from death's door makes you think... whether you want to or not, it's inevitable to sit and wonder what would have happened if you had died. Just in a split of a second... everything would have ended.

Your life, your relationships and all those dreams and goals that you had been working towards... all gone just like that.

But would it have mattered?

Death – the end of a life – it happens, it's inevitable in some cases, but what we forget is it is a part of life rather than the end of it.

I've never been scared of death... but having had a near-death experience scares you, not of death but of time, the time that you have been given in this life and the most fear I feel now is when I think about the time I have left. We don't realize just how much time we waste in life, holding grudges, having fights and maintaining distance from those that have either hurt us or rather some that we have hurt and are too scared to apologise.

One thing I have always believed in and even more so now that – *Life Is Too Short*.

Life is short, unpredictable and full of surprises. You just never know what's around the corner. One minute it's all great and the next minute you can end up at death's door – scared not of death but of not being able to say goodbye because of not having time, or rather not getting a chance because your one way flight is already booked.

Standing between life and death – I was scared I hadn't said goodbye, I hadn't been able to pass on my responsibilities, I hadn't been able to make sure my parents would be okay without me, that my best friend who is more than a sister would have someone now that my time was up and most importantly that I hadn't been able to say, "I love you," to all those that I truly loved and lived for.

If you look at them, they're just three tiny words but hold so much more meaning and value than what is just on the surface. Love – a very strong word and precious emotion – those that have experienced love are lucky. I've always believed in never loving at all rather than loving and losing. And it scared me that I would never have been able to tell those that I deeply adored that I loved them if death hadn't given me a second chance.

But what if it hadn't? Would it have mattered because the truth is that life goes on no matter what; life doesn't stop for anyone and yes not even for death. People would mourn for a day or two and then forget that I ever existed. Though they say that those near our heart will always stay in the heart even after death. Who knows... I guess time will tell someday.

However, what does matter is how I live life now, now that I've had a second chance at life. As they say live life to the fullest, buy that handbag, book that once in a lifetime holiday, eat that piece of cake and drink that wine – you never know... how much life is left. Money comes and goes... never stop making memories whilst you're still alive because once you're gone you'll be 'a memory'.

Things to do before you die!

Life is way too short... so live life to the fullest, buy that expensive handbag, eat that cake, drink up that wine and book that spontaneous holiday! In life there are many times and moments that simply take your breath away – places that you go, views that you see, people that you meet and the achievements that you never ever dreamt of.

There are people who do things in order to live life but some of us crazy lot do things in order to tick off the list of things to do before we die – so here's mine:

1. Get lost in Las Vegas, exploring the different extravagant hotels that each have their unique touch and interior; especially getting lost in the unique fountain show at the Bellagio. It is often said after pondering the Grand Canyon for the first time, most visitors are stunned into a deep silence and the problem isn't the lack of words but more that the canyon is so vast and so deep that the vista stretches so far across anyone's line of vision.

2. Get to know the Germans and their unlimited supply of German beer and delicious Bratwurst and Schnitzel. Learn the funniest and most unique German phrases with them – my most favourite is the one that personifies Monday's our favourite days of the week and as it goes – 'Montag ist ein Arschloch'. Explore the exciting and full of surprises nightlife of Berlin, explore the German beauty in the south and most scenic part of Germany – Heidelburg. The tall and somewhat beautiful financial sector in Frankfurt and Dusseldorf will also take your breath away despite it being a business hub.

3. Shop till you drop in one of the most popular shopping destinations – New York – the city that never sleeps. Don't forget to watch a Broadway show that will leave you breathless and gasping for more – the magic and the incredible performances. Take a stroll by the Hudson River – enjoy the breath-taking views looking across at the city that never sleeps. Walk around Wall Street, taking in all the moneymaking machines around you. Grab some food from the delicious food vendors after a night out in the party district of the city that literally never sleeps. Walk around Time Square at a time where

there's no one there. Snap a picture and cherish those memories. Be an utter tourist!

4. Hanoi – Vietnam: One of the most beautiful places on this earth with its breath-taking beauty and unbelievably nice people. They have the most beautiful caves though, filled with bats that give you the best photographs ever. Their unique and tasty delicacies are known around the world, so unique and different not just in the way they cook but also their choice of ingredients.

5. Thailand – a country that is rich with not only culture but values and traditions that are unbelievable. Their King died and the whole country mourned like it was someone in their family that had died and they still are and apparently will be for a whole year. I mean we don't even do that for our own sometimes. It also has some of the most beautiful beaches on this earth, especially James Bond Island where yes the movie was shot. You can actually see your whole body in the clear water. The gorgeous shades of the clear blue water are just so breath-taking that it makes you actually wonder if all this is real. Thai people are a funny bunch, simply because they are always happy, they are so nice to you; even if they can't speak proper English they will still be so kind and willing to help you. And I'm proud to say that even though just for a short four months – this amazing country was my home.

An unimaginable loss

Every pain at some point or another in life will heal but losing a child is a pain that you have to live with for the rest of your life. Losing a child is an unimaginable loss for a parent and it is not something they can ever forget, it is something they have to learn to live with for the rest of their lives. At times we feel awkward or over sensitive when talking to someone who has lost a child, we feel like we shouldn't mention their child's name because the parent might feel sad and talking about their dead child might remind them of him or her. But truth is the death of your child is not something you forget... ever and so there is not point tip-toeing around someone who has lost a child.

Perhaps talking to them and listening to them talk about their child might be one of the best things you can do for them. Because the truth is there aren't many people that will be by your side during your time of need and loss. It's funny how they say that you find out your real friends and those true to you in your darkest hours. And they only say it because it is true, there will be many that will be by your side in your good and successful times but hardly any that will be by your side when you don't have that million dollar house anymore, that Mercedes which they loved getting a ride in or that amazing job.

Any loss in life is tough, unbearable and becomes a lifetime of melancholia for the one going through it, but losing a child is something no one can imagine but the parent. There are parents who find out their child has a life-threatening disease a few days after they are born, those active and sporty kids that are diagnosed with cancer out of the blue and then those that lose their lives to fate – whether it be a rollercoaster gone wrong, or the result of a drunk driver not knowing how to drive safely.

Death in life is inevitable, many say that death is the end of life but the truth is death is a part of life. Life is a heartless and cold bitch because the truth is life goes on no matter what. The world could be ending for someone because they've lost everything when they've lost their child in a car accident or lost their battle with cancer but the bitter truth is that life doesn't stop for anyone and especially not for death. Life keeps going on and with life we have to do the same. When a parent loses a child, it is a long and emotional process. It begins the very minute the child has passed away and only ends on the day when the parent joins them.

The Last Battle – Her versus C

She was a beautiful, kind-hearted, selfless yet ambitious young lady. Every emotion with her was passionate. She didn't know how to do moderate or be neutral. It was either love or hate. There was no grey area with her.

Balance – could be used as another name for her; whether this was work and life balance, work and relationships or any other two factors that are important. What she could never balance was her love. Love meant everything to her. For her love was life even before she knew what love was, what it means, what it does to people and how it impacts lives.

She did everything for her love, her passion, her drive in life. Things any normal girl wouldn't really do... but she did. But then again she wasn't normal, she was a fighter, she was a beautiful girl yet a bit boyish. After all she had learnt how to be her own hero because life had left her no choice.

She won every battle in life no matter how hard, how long, how painful... but... there was one battle she couldn't win. She always believed that love and death always come uninvited in life. On one hand, love was her life; she wanted to be loved the way she loved, fiercely, unconditionally, truly, deeply and fearlessly. And on the other hand, this girl wasn't scared of death. She embraced death like one embraces a loved one.

She always said death doesn't scare her; love does, because that is the only thing in this world that has the power to completely destroy a person to the point where nothing can help them survive.

She knew this battle would kill her as if her love wasn't enough to do the job but she never said a word, nothing. Never grumbled. Never complained to God or questioned Him.

But... she looked up and smiled at God – thanked him for the blessings He had given her in life and for an amazing life she believed she lived despite the melancholia. And then... with an even bigger smile said... "I'll see you soon".

But there was only one thing she wanted before she let her guard down, and that was to see her love and say goodbye. And she got that opportunity, to see, feel, experience her life – her love... but for some reason she didn't say goodbye. She just left taking all those memories that they had together adding them to this last time, smiled at her love... with her eyes tearing up... saying goodbye in her heart and not out loud and turned away. Thanking God once again for the last time before...

... losing her battle. The girl that never lost any challenge, that never gave up when life got tough or lost any fight in life... lost her first ever battle not with or against life but against death; the one thing that didn't scare her. She battled for a prolonged time of 25 months what felt like 25 years with Mr C aka cancer and in the end lost.

For the first time ever... she lost.

The Last Battle – RIP – Part 2

Though she lost her first ever battle in life against Mr C; she wasn't forgotten. After all, she was the life and beat of many. A girl that was the life of a party, the sunshine they called her along with being little Miss Giggles.

For the first time ever, her phone was off. For the first time ever, she didn't message him after that meeting. For the first time ever, she didn't ask him to text her when he would get home safe. He did find that strange but didn't question her about it; male ego after all. He found it strange that he didn't hear from her for a whole week after they had met. She wasn't like that; she was very considerate, friendly and kind-hearted. She had always asked about his well-being and made sure he was home safe before she slept at night... but that night that didn't happen. It didn't happen because she was no longer there to ask him if he had got home alright or to say anything anymore. She was gone. God had only kept her alive so she could say goodbye to her love. So she could see him and talk to him and smile at him one last time.

But he didn't know that. He didn't know that the girl who was always there for him; no matter what, was no longer going to be there. She was the person who loved him the most in this whole wide world, it could be argued that her love for him was more than his own mother's love for him. She was crazy in love with him, the kind of love where you think about the one you love before yourself, the one where you can't sleep at night knowing they are not okay, the one where you cry in your prayers for them, for their happiness, for their wellbeing, for their success.

People looked at him in disgust for being so oblivious and heartless to her presence but then again she did believe that if her presence didn't matter to him, neither would her absence and that is exactly what happened. She was gone and he didn't know. Then one day... a day before her birthday to be exact, he found out from a Facebook page that had been made by some of the children she used to volunteer for – showing pictures of her teaching them, playing with them and just being there for them. The pictures made him smile without realising, until he read the three letters that shook his entire world – RIP.

The phone dropped from his hand and he felt a big lump in his throat. He knew this – He finally did – the only girl who truly loved him was now gone. Dead. She was never coming back. Shockingly for most – he fell to the ground and felt a tear roll down his face. He wasn't sure what was going on or how he was feeling. He couldn't believe she was gone for good. He took advantage of her always being there for him and now the only person who he could count on – was gone.

That's life. We don't see or accept it but that is exactly what life is about. We always lose the one person that we take for granted or don't appreciate. It's true how they say – we only realize what we had when it's gone. The next day – he went to visit her. The grave could hardly be seen under the mountain of flowers – he took her lilies – white lilies. She had always joked about how she wanted white lilies for her funeral and red roses when she was alive. He remembered. Her soul smiled when she saw the lilies. The heartless cold stone actually listened when she spoke – much to the surprise of both of them.

He fell to the ground – crying – screaming – holding the gravestone as though he could make her come back to life again but he couldn't. She was gone. It was him – he killed her. Not cancer.

The memories of all her acts of kindness and love flash backed in front of his very eyes as he sat there mourning the death of 'The One' – she had gotten away. And there he was – by her grave... wishing. Wishing he had seen her for who she was. Wishing he hadn't hurt her the way he did. Wishing he had given her the love she deserved. Wishing she would come back just one last time so he could make things right. Wishing he could see her radiant smile one last time – the smile that made his heart melt – though he never admitted it. But that's all he had left were wishes – wishes that would never be fulfilled.

Live. Love. Laugh. Learn. Before it's too late.

One Shot – Dead and Gone

All it takes is one shot and you're dead and gone. Just one shot to end a life. You never know when you'll be shot or be the victim of gun crime or race crime. People carry guns these days like it's nothing. Just another accessory to carry. They don't realize the damage it can do. Not sure if I should call it damage... because at least after damage has been done... some repair can be made. But not with life. Once you're shot – there's no coming back.

I wonder how heartless and ruthless you would have to be to just pull that trigger. I think twice before killing a bug that bites me, but we live in a world where people don't think even once before pulling the trigger on a gun.

Gun crime is the norm in the US with Americans owning 300 million guns – that means there is one available for every member of the population. There are mass shootings, school shootings, race crime, stereotype hatred and many more in the US. A country so big with so many people from every walk of life – yet so much hate.

God has made every one of us in a different way – even English people change colours once they are tanned so why do they hate brown people or black people? The amount of black shootings due to racism shocks me and breaks my heart. We are all human beings just different colours – wouldn't it be boring if we were all the same colour?

What if your friend was hanging out with you, living life to the max one minute and the next day you get a text message that they're gone. Not even a single call, not even a goodbye, not even a 'take care'. Just one text, one word; dead. Gone. Brings a lump to your throat doesn't it? You can't imagine it because they're your friend. You hung out together. You partied together. They were your 'bro'! You can't even imagine a day without them. They're the person you call when Bae's acting up or when something big happens. When you hit the jackpot or are drunk at 4am and need to tell someone how sexy their pizza looks!

But what do you do when you just get those three letters? RIP.

Have you ever imagined what your friend, your love or anyone close to you would feel the minute they find out that you're no more? Would they care? Would they cry? Would they find the bastard who killed you? Would they mourn for a day and move on?

For those who've never experienced it, I hope that you don't but death leaves a heartache no one can heal. The only tiny bit of peace it brings with it is that our loved one is now in a much better place and hopefully we will be seeing them soon. For me it's way better than losing someone in life because with death at least you know there's no coming back and it wasn't a choice – but with people that walk out of your life – it's their pick – their choice. And that hurts way more than losing someone to death.

I didn't know this guy but somehow my heart broke a little when I found out that he had passed away – actually not passed away but been killed. Killed brutally by a gunshot. He was 26 – he had his whole life ahead of him. So much to do, so many aspirations, so many dreams; all of them just gone. Just like that; but that's life I guess. One minute you're breathing and the next minute you're gone.

He died in Las Vegas – a place very close to my heart. All I feel is pain and disgust at the world we live in – that is filled with so much hatred and crime. At least he is in a much better place now where no harm can reach him. I know for sure he was loved and is deeply missed. Hope you rest in peace bro. See you soon!

Car Crash – Death's Door

'If you would indeed behold the spirit of death, open your heart wide unto the body of life. For life and death are one, even as the river and the sea are one.'
– Khalil Gibran.

Normally we do not like to think about death, we run away from the idea like the plague. We would rather think about life, what we have done and what more there is still to do. So why reflect on death? When you start preparing for death you soon realize that you must look into your life... now... and come to face the truth of yourself. Death is like a mirror in which the true meaning of life is reflected.

Not many of us can say we have had a near-death experience, a time where you're at death's door but are lucky or fortunate enough to return. And then there are those that do not return. For those that know me personally and inside out know that death isn't something I'm scared of, in fact it is something I embrace with open arms as I would a loved one. I'm the girl that everyone knows lives life to the fullest – my motto has always been to live each day like it's my last.

But I never ever had imagined or thought to have been so close to that last day, a day that could have been my last, a day that I'll always remember as the day when I literally came back from death's door. It was a normal Thursday, I had gone to work and had a pretty good day and was on my way back where I was stationary in my car with my indicators on, indicating and waiting to turn right. It was 8.15pm, late in the evening and I was roughly a mile away from home, I had had a good day at work and was looking forward to being home soon to share it all with my mum. Little did I know that something would happen that would mean that I might not see my mum ever again.

As I was stationary on the right side of the road, just about to turn all I heard was a huge bang! I had been hit from the back so hard, with such a huge impact by the car behind me – speeding – that it meant my car took a full 180 degree turn throwing me on the opposite side of the road. And as if this wasn't enough, it was a busy road and there was on-coming traffic from the other side of the road where I had been pushed in my car due to the hit. Not being able to understand what had just happened – the first thing I saw in my rear mirror was a huge HGV lorry coming towards me – not stopping but rather honking at me. I had just been hit by a speeding car and was then about to be hit by a lorry – even now a day later all I see flashbacks of is that lorry about to hit me.

Despite my many unintentional attempts at death where I've been clumsy or crossed the road without looking, I always thought that I'm the girl who cannot die or so that God doesn't want me yet – because I've not fulfilled my purpose in life. But this incident really made this notion come true because what happened that night was not survivable. There was no way I could have survived after that lorry had eaten me up.

But I guess one's good deeds and the prayers of our loved ones do work and that is what saved me that night. Somehow

I managed to move my car out of the busy oncoming traffic filled road and didn't become a prey to that lorry, a lorry that seemed so thirsty of my blood. Somehow I managed to come back from death's door. Somehow, just somehow I got another chance at life.

I know I must be grateful and yes I am but I can't help but wonder what could have happened, I can't help but wonder why it happened, why that lorry hadn't stopped and had gotten so close to me, I can't help but visualize that lorry in my rear view mirror.

Everything we buy today comes with some sort of guarantee for a year or more, but one thing we forget is that life comes with no guarantee – having been so close to that just two days ago has made me realize just how precious life is and how much we take it for granted. Life is a journey that should be enjoyed and lived to the max! Something I have always lived by – hence, I travel as much as I can, I do as much as I can in one day and yes some may call it a tiring and hectic life, but I call it a happy and fulfilling life because I do things that make me happy, I spend it with people that appreciate and love me and I am thankful, thankful to God for the smallest to the biggest gifts in life that he has blessed me with. And now I have a second life to thank Him for.

Bereavement – Adjusting to loss they say

The definition of a bereavement is adjusting to the loss of a loved one... but do we ever really adjust to loss? Do we? Does the agony of loss ever go away? Do we ever forget that we've lost a loved one? Someone that was a huge part of our life until just a minute ago?

All it takes is a minute or even less for our entire life to change. I always believe that in life; 'Love and Death' are the only two things that come uninvited.

You're gone... just like that. God took you away from us. Why did He do that I sometimes wonder? You were so young.

You had so much to do. We had so much to do. I miss you. I wish you were still here. I wish I had gone instead of you. You know death doesn't scare me. I would right this minute swap places with you if I could but He didn't want me, He wanted you. I'll never know why.

I feel broken... numb... lost... incomplete without you. At times I feel emotionless and at others as if there is an ocean of tears that just won't stop flowing. You always called me a strong woman but I don't agree. If I am as strong as you always said why do I feel at my weakest right now? Why do I feel like I'll never get over losing you? Why do I feel so broken like I've never felt before?

Do you know I looked up to God today and asked him, questioned him, pleaded with him... just for you? It is so cruel for you to be just taken away like this. If I am so grief–stricken I can't even imagine how everyone else might feel. But that's the thing about grief; about pain... everyone deals with it differently.

I really miss you... I really do. I wish there was something I could do to bring you back to me... anything... I would do it. I would even give up my own life for you. I wish He had given us some more time... to at least say goodbye properly. I won't say I wish I can get over the loss of losing you but I do hope that one day I can remember you and miss you with a smile rather than a waterfall flowing from my eyes. I still remember how you made fun of me... but yes losing you has left with me just them... lots of tears and I am sorry. I know you hate my tears but I don't know how to stop them anymore. I don't know how to not miss you. I just want one more day with you and I promise I won't ask for more. Please ask Him to give you back to me. I can't live without you.

Bereavement – will I ever adjust to this loss?

Life doesn't stop for anyone.

Human nature is funny isn't it... we always want what we don't have... and when we do have it, we don't appreciate it.

Life... the happy or sad thing sometimes, about it... is that it doesn't stop for anyone.

No matter what happens... life goes on... it could be a death, a bereavement, a loss, a divorce... anything. When we lose someone or something we love we feel like it's the end of the world. Truth is: yes we feel down, broken and lost when it happens but life does go on. We do return to normality. And that is the truth. Yes it hurts, but the truth always does.

Sometimes we don't realize this truth... whether it's coming back to work after being off for a few weeks, meeting an old friend after months or returning back to your home land after years. In our own selfish way we expect that everything will be the same but it isn't is it?

Your life might have changed a lot in those few days, months or even years but so has the lives of those around you. They've moved on too and as hard as that is to accept – it is the truth.

It's strange though how things change... at times, the people you were really close to before you left, couldn't care less about you anymore. After all we do live in a nasty, horrible world full of only selfish people. People who only want to use and abuse you.

The truth about distance though is that you learn a lot about people – those that are true to you and those that are just there for you when they really only need something from you – which makes me laugh.

Over the years, one thing I have learnt is that there's a huge reason behind people leaving – people come into our life for a reason, someone once told me, they're either a lesson or a blessing. I'm glad to have learnt this lesson – no need to chase people – their part in your movie has ended.

Life's too short...

Life's too short... it really is... though often I find myself saying... this life is really long... a bit too long for my liking at times but the bitter truth is that life's too short indeed.

Sometimes way too short... for a baby dying at four days due to being born premature... or a young child dying at the age of four as a result of leukaemia, a teenager dying at the age of 14 due to a drunk driver causing a hit and run, your science teacher dying at 40 due to unexpected cancer with no evident symptoms until he had reached the last stage.

Truth is we never really know when our time may come... we could be happy today... just graduated, just been married, just had a baby, just got a new job and then the very next day we could be gone... there are many incidents happening around us that could cause our death but we never think about any of them. I guess its human nature; we always worry about tomorrow, the next day and the future. We always worry about work tomorrow, how to entertain the kids during the holidays, how to get that big promotion at work, how to get that one girl/guy to like us and amongst all this we forget just how precious life is... and the unknown duration of it.

Why is it that we humans are so ungrateful for everything we have? It might sound a cliché but the food in our bellies, access to clean water, a roof over our heads with loving and caring families, amazing true friends, a good well paid job, a car that makes it easy to go from A to B ... and the list just never ends.

Then why is it that it takes something huge for us to acknowledge any of the above things, why is it always that human beings need 'a shock to the system' as I call it, to realize just how short life is and just how grateful we should be for everything that we are blessed with.

Yes, it hurts when things don't go our way or we don't get something or someone we really wanted, needed and at times thought we couldn't live without. But the sad truth in life is that as much as it hurts, life goes on. Life is a journey that doesn't stop for anyone... whether it's losing someone who is alive or losing someone to death. We may feel like life has stopped and we can't carry on anymore but we always do... somehow... we always do in the end – because this life doesn't stop for anyone.

Why is it that hospitals have seen truer promises and confessions than a church or a mosque? Why is it that people only wake up when they're about to lose someone they truly love? Why is it that death has to be on your door for you to realize where you're going with your life? Why is it that graveyards receive more flowers than those houses where people can actually receive them in their hands? Why? Why do people only realize how much someone meant to them once they're gone and it's too late?

This life is way too short for grudges, petty arguments, being upset with the one you love over small mistakes that don't actually matter in the bigger picture called life. Call, message or even email the one you love, care about – whether it's a lover, friend or family – tell them how you feel before it's too late. Don't be stingy with your words whether its feelings or forgiveness – because truth is you won't have any left for their funeral. If you really want someone or something, go after it! Give it your all, because this life's too short for tomorrows!

Just like shops, people can be closed

I don't know what to do... I've been going crazy out of my mind.

I wish I could just talk to you, ask you how you are, because God knows it's killing me slowly not knowing. I wish you would just talk to me... life's' too short to hold grudges. We both made mistakes... I apologised because I realized I was wrong and didn't want to lose you. I wish you would too... I wish you knew just how long I've waited for your apology. You made me feel like you were fixing me but the truth is you crushed me into more pieces than I already was and left me even more broken.

But I still miss you... I loved you after all. You meant so much to me... all the memories, the laughs, the tears, the movies, the hugs, the food that we cooked for each other, the day you painted my nails for me, the time I ironed your work shirt for you, the day you brought me a brownie to cheer me up... I can go on and on just like the tears in my eyes right now.

I'm trying... I really am trying to forget you... to learn how to forget the bad and remember the good memories and smile back at them rather than ending up in a flood of tears each time. But truth is though I'm learning to smile... it doesn't seem to be working. We created way too many memories to be able to forget and move on from them so easily.

I just wish you'd talk to me one last time. We had way too much to just part ways like this... I pray and hope that you understand this one day.

I can't begin to explain how I long to hear your voice and to talk to you for hours on end just like we used to... we always had so much to talk about, so much to share... I still remember the day we spoke on the phone for nearly four hours... about anything and everything.

I know you were always closed off about your feelings, but I never ever imagined you would just shut off from me like this... like a closed shop but one that seems to have closed forever. I know you blame me for a number of things but trust me, none of it can match up to the guilt that I live with daily, but surely you could find it in your heart to forgive me, the same heart that claimed to be the place where I live or shall I say lived according to you. Why can't we just forgive and forget and move on? Why is it that just like always you let your anger get the best of you? Why is it that your insecurities have torn us apart? I was stupid enough to think I could help you but your aggressive nature wasn't a part-time thing... it was more a lifetime of anger bottled up that only lashed out at me. Was it because I made you to see things you refused to acknowledge otherwise? Was it because I was the only person who was realistic and practical with you? And not someone who lived in a fantasy world and believed every delusional comment you made?

We may not be a part of each other's lives anymore... but I do wish that you let go of all your anger and built-up aggression inside you and enjoy life because this life is too precious to be lived or rather suffered in just anger. Maybe one day you'll know why I was trying to help you open up and let go off your anger... and maybe just maybe that one day will be too late...

Quandary – There is nothing certain, but the uncertain

There is nothing more stressful than dealing with uncertainty.

Not knowing what's next or what to do next is something most of us don't deal with very well. After all how are you meant to when you've always had everything planned and organised in your life to the very minute... and then boom! You have no idea what's next... absolutely no clue.

And you know what's worse is that there is nothing you can do about it... it's just a waiting game and that's what makes it so much more harder... so much more painful. For example, having had a really busy life with university, multiple part-time jobs, a post-graduate degree and a fixed term contract role and then once it ends... nothing. You have nothing to do... nothing to look forward to until you find another job and that's hard... because finding a job isn't that easy... especially not in today's job market. It takes a lot of time, effort and endless applications until you hit the right jackpot.

Another example can be being in a stable and happy rela-tionship which isn't leading anywhere... the world doesn't understand but both men and women need stability, commit-ment and a promise – a promise that the one they love, does and will always love them back – a promise that they will build a life together, a happy one – a promise that they will stick by each other in every happiness and sorrow and never leave each other's side.

Some say that nothing in this world causes as much misery as uncertainty. Those fighting for their lives and not knowing whether they'll make it... deal with the highest level of uncertainty – imagine not knowing if you'll live or even worse not knowing how close death is. I think that alone is enough to kill you.

However, through this tough time in life not many people have anyone to turn to – to share their sorrow with, to be able to hear that 'everything will be okay soon' and that is the sad truth of life – it is indeed that when we really need someone, no one is there. And the people we need the most only realize just how much we needed them when it's too late and they're telling the world how much they regret it standing at the altar before their loved one's coffin.

Life – the sum of all your choices

Decisions are the hardest thing to make especially when it is a choice between where you should be and where you want to be. In life, most of the time we must make a choice to take a chance or our life will never change. But each of these choices has a huge impact on our lives and especially our futures, which is something most of us don't realize or understand at the time.

Our lives are full of choices... choices that we make in our everyday lives and choices that we make that change our everyday lives forever. These can be life choices, lifestyle choices, career choices, life partner choices, pet choices and one of the most important ones, choosing friends... those friends that often become our family. It is only when we grow up that we realize that every choice that we make has and will in the future have an impact on our overall lives. I've just realized that now... after years of bad, wrong and some even stupid choices the effect they have had on my life, my future actions and the way I think now.

One of the most important decisions we make in life is choosing a career. It is very important that the choice we make is one that makes us happy, will motivate us to wake up in the morning and want to actually go to work, one where we'll enjoy the work that we do in our daily job. It is important to actually enjoy the job that we choose for ourselves as a career rather than simply do it for the money because the motivation for money outgrows the motivation for an actually career.

First for some but the second most important decision for me in life is the decision of choosing a life partner – choosing the one person who you want to spend the rest of your life with. One that will make everything okay the minute they walk into your life. I say it is a huge decision and a choice that we have to live with for the rest of our lives simply because a life partner isn't just a wife or a husband, it's your new best friend, a life-long one, your partner in crime, your lover, your life support 24/7 and someone who will accept you for who you are along with any baggage that you come with, someone who will not ridicule you if things go wrong, won't raise their hand on you in an argument and will treat you with respect at all times.

My mother always says and it is true in life too, love can't get you far in life but when someone respects you... happiness will automatically follow. For me personally, another very important choice is about making friends; being an only daughter, most of my close friends are like sisters to me but choosing friends is a very important choice too – because true friends not only enter your lives, but your heart as well as your home. And if they aren't who they say they are or aren't genuine then they can ruin everything. I was betrayed by someone I called my best friend and sister and know just how much that hurts. Hence, it is important to see that just like any other relationship, friendship is a two-way street too, where there is honesty, trust and most importantly loyalty. I didn't know this until now but the people you choose as your friends can have a huge impact on you, your life and most unexpectedly your future so choose your partner in crime and a bestie wisely!

Make good and wise choices today so you don't have to live with regrets tomorrow!

A ray of sunshine

You know those days that just start off crap... like you know you don't want them to start before they even have... those are one of the toughest ones to get through. And sometimes no matter how hard you try you just can't seem to hide it... it's so evident on your face that even the security guard downstairs can tell and he doesn't even know you... but he can tell from the pain decorated beautifully on your face, the bags under your eyes and the constant struggle your lips are going through in order to crack a smile.

So how do you deal with it? What do you do? Who do you turn to? How do you manage to crack a smile and make that smile actually look like its genuine? Like how? Why is it so tough?

Is it ever going to get better? Will the smiling ever get easier or be genuine again? Then as you're going on with your day... something happens or someone comes along who makes you smile again – you realize that life's too short to even miss a single chance to smile.

A smile is the only curve that can set everything straight

And yes I believe that too... despite struggling to smile most days.

So today was one of those days for me and believe it or not nothing was helping, even my favourite song couldn't do the trick, but then came along a cute little boy, he's only 10 years old, my student that I tutor who just without even trying made me smile... a genuine smile spread across my face. Because that's what kids do, they make the world a better place without even knowing or trying.

It could be anything or anyone that comes into your life and helps you crack that smile that has been struggling to reach your eyes all day long and at times for days. Be thankful because not everyone is fortunate or shall I say lucky enough to have that ray of sunshine brighten up your day.

Is it really that hard to say sorry?

Doesn't love mean doing anything for the one you love? Like anything? Then why is it so hard to say sorry? And not just for no reason, for actually hurting and destroying the one you love? When we claim to love someone, not all of us actually mean it. Because if everyone who claimed to love someone truly meant it, there wouldn't be two people in this world who wouldn't be together nor would their love end.

I don't get when people say, 'I don't love you anymore' or 'he/she fell out of love'. Like how? How do you stop loving someone you claimed to love the most in this world? I don't get it. You either love someone or you don't... there's no falling out of love. Yes you might move on from them but the truth is a tiny part of you will always love them.

And surely if you truly love someone and have deeply hurt them, you'd apologise rather than hold on to your stubbornness and ego. I mean people apologise to the one they love even if they're not in the wrong, just to save their relationship and not lose them. But some unfortunate souls have to live with the fact that someone who claims to love them and worships the ground we walk on wouldn't apologise for destroying their entire soul and that hurts, in fact it kills. And what's even worse is that we continue to love them despite them not being sorry... not being sorry or having any remorse for decorating your soul with wounds that have left lifelong scars on not only your body but your mind, heart and soul. Scars and pains that you have to live with and some don't... or shall I say can't... some of us struggle big time to live with it all.

And then comes a point in what might seem like a never ending melancholy, where you realize that even if they do apologise, it will only take you back... back to them... back to a point where you were weak and they had the power to destroy you... and you don't want to go back there. And that is the exact moment you realize that you don't need anything from them anymore. Apart from closure, so you do that one last thing that gives you peace and allows you to close that chapter of your life forever. It's not really a sorry we're after but more... a closure! A closure that is important in order for us to survive... for us to carry on with this life rather than end up dead with them crying by our graveside. One thing I will say though is that saying sorry doesn't make you small or isn't an act of belittling anyone... it is simply an act only done by those with immense strength and a heart that actually feels emotion.

Hard work always pays off

There will be obstacles. There will be doubters. There will be mistakes. But with hard work, there are no limits. Many a time there are phases in life where no matter what you do, nothing seems to work out, you seem to be doing all the right things but there is no reward to reap or no positive outcome of all the graft you have put in to achieve what you want. And then after a very long time, a lot of hard work and sweat, sleepless nights, long day... there comes a ray of sunshine where all of that pays off. You finally are given the reward to reap and achieve your goals. And that point all the waiting doesn't mean anything... because that sigh of relief means so much more.

A lot of what separates those who want and those who have is the simple fact that one stopped while the other kept going. In life there will be many obstacles that you will have to face, many challenges that will break you, many moments where you will start to lose faith and give up but don't because you remember why you held on for so long.

Things always work out in the end, it may not always be the outcome that you've wanted but it will always be what is right for you and where God wants you to be; may it be where you end up geographically in life, the job you land or the person you end up spending the rest of your life with. Because indeed God is the best planner of all and knows what is best for us.

Just never lose your faith; it's amazing how far just a little bit of faith will go. Work hard, do your best and leave the rest to Him. There is no way that you won't get what He has written for you and neither will you get any less than what He has written for you.

Will it ever get better?

My chest started to tighten up at around 11pm... I had had a good day with some great news that I had been waiting over two months for and had been happy all day. Though the truth is when I got the good news, you were the first person I wanted to tell after my parents. I wish you understood how I feel and just how much you mean to me... I know a lot has happened between us for you not to believe my feelings but surely actions speak louder than words right? Surely whenever there's doubt in your mind and heart, you can remember the things I did for you and only for you. I still remember the day I walked in heavy rain just to get your wallet engraved. You were even mad at me for getting home late after going to the gym but what could I have done? I had finally found the place that did engraving. I was so excited for the engraving and to give you your present... do you remember the amount of times I asked you like a baby if I could give it to you early? Simply because I couldn't wait.

Your birthday is just round the corner again... and it's hard for me... it's hard because this time last year we were together... I was excited about giving you your special presents... about spending your birthday with you... about being the first person to wish you a happy birthday. And here we are today, we don't talk... you didn't even contact me on your birthday... that really hurt... and I know you were surprised as to why I would expect you to and neither do I... but my heart did and I can't control my heart right. It hurts to know there is no chance of me ever seeing you again, or us celebrating your birthday together again... and that hurts... it hurts like hell. I can't tell you just how much I'm hurting right now and what hurts me even more is that you blame me for my hurt.

I just wish I knew if it'll ever get better... will I ever stop hurting? Will I ever stop missing you? Will I ever stop feeling like you're missing from me?

How do you live with NO ANSWERS?

The more I think of it the more I realize. There are no answers. Life is to be lived. How do you do it? How do you live with no answers?

How do you go on with life not knowing? Not knowing why something happened to you? That something could either be good or bad... but we need answers. When something terrible happens... we break... at times incidents that happen shatter us and we have no bloody idea why that happened to us? Especially when we did nothing to deserve it! That's when it hurts the most.

How do we go on from that though? Living without answers can kill a person inside... a slow death that is spreading like poison in your body. Why did he leave me when he said he never would? When he said he couldn't live without me? Why did he lay his hands on me when he loved the bones off of me? How could he do that? Is physical abuse love? Is that what love is for him?

Why did my father leave my mother? Why did their marriage never work when my mum did everything to make him happy? To be with a man who didn't deserve a great woman like her? Why did I get stopped at the airport? Was it the colour of my skin or the scarf on my head? Why can't I do as well as my siblings did at school? Why do I suffer from anxiety? Why do I feel depressed?

These are just some of the many questions people live with day in day out? Without any concrete answers to any of these questions? How do they do it? Why can't we get answers to any of these questions? Why can't people just be honest before leaving you? Before breaking your heart? Do they have any idea how hard it is living and carrying on with life without any answers?

No they certainly don't but I do hope that they do realize one day just how much their one apology could fix things or most importantly, fix people.

I need more time, I want more time...

Before she went into the operating theatre, she was scared for her life... but not for herself but for him and for her family. She needed more time... more time to help them learn how to live without her. When someone dies they don't die alone, something dies in those that are the loved ones of the deceased, something deep down dies in their hearts that used to be filled with love. We don't die alone, we cause a death in the home that we lived in and a numbness in the hearts of those that love us, a pain in the lives of those that were and will always be connected with us – a pain that never goes away.

I always believe love and death always come into our lives uninvited. However, there are those that know that their death is near and hence, want to make sure that before they leave they make things easier for those that they are leaving behind. *My Sister's Keeper* – the movie is a perfect example of a sister making sure her younger sister is safe and healthy and is not being used as a scapegoat for her cancer.

There is an old woman who due to a fall experienced a brain bleed which was going to kill her within the next few hours, only brain surgery could save her life or should I say buy her more time. Her husband was against the surgery, he had been a surgeon all his life, simply because he knew she wouldn't survive it and there would be many complications. However, the old woman decided against it and wanted the surgery because being a medic too in her younger days she knew only the surgery could buy her some more time – she needed more time because when she had the fall, she didn't know that it would lead her to her death. She needed more time to help her husband learn how to live without her – She was 95 years of age and they had a happy and beautiful marriage of 60 years. They both didn't know how to live without each other. And so she needed more time and also wanted it because... 60 years just weren't enough time.

Surviving death can either be a blessing or a curse... if you survive you basically get another chance at life which is a blessing because not a lot of people get another chance and aren't fortunate enough to live. However, then there are those that survive accidents and life threatening experiences and literally return from death's door. But how do you go on with life after experiencing that? How do you come out of that state of shock?

Returning from death's door is a traumatising experience – one they say you never really come back from the same. Because you really don't. You're not the same person anymore. But the positive thing is that at least yes, you survived. But also that you see things very differently now... your perspective towards life is completely different. You view things in a new light now. You realize that life really is very precious... it is unpredictable for sure but it is also very short and hence should be lived to the fullest. Do everything that you have on your bucket list before it is too late. Tomorrow isn't promised to anyone.

And you know what the truth is... we regret more the things that we didn't do than those that we did. Buy that bag, eat that cake, drink that wine and most of all tell the ones you love just how much you do so because you never know if you'll get the chance again.

Having returned from death's door – I don't know yet whether it's a blessing for me or a curse but I'm figuring it out slowly but surely. But one thing I do know is that I need a little more time and also I want a bit more time – still lots to do – things I want to tick off, places I want to see, career goals I want to achieve and maybe give happiness and love another chance before the end date.

My Motto – Live Each Day Like It's Your Last

Death of a friendship – was it worth it?

We all have problems in life but letting our personal issues take over our relationships and most importantly friendships isn't exactly the best way to deal with it. Friends they say are like medicine for the wounded heart and vitamins for a hopeful soul. In life, we can't choose our family and hence God gave us friends because the truth is true friends are more than family; at least for me. For those who live away from their family or live alone, the friends they make become the family we are away from and miss.

Lucky are those who have a few true friends who are always there for them; in sickness and in health, in happiness and in sorrow, in the brightness of light and in the days filled with darkness and those are the ones worth holding on to. Then there are those that have a lot of friends but only when it suits them, it is said that if you have people during your darkest hours; those are the ones worth a lot more than 100 friends who are there when you have a party to throw.

I was lucky enough, or at least I thought I was, to have found a friend who very quickly became a best friend and then someone I considered a sister, a partner in crime and somewhat my life. However, the truth is not everyone you love or care about understands your emotions and feelings. At times a friendship begins and ends only to serve a purpose; after all not everyone you meet in life is meant to be a permanent fixture in your life.

Truth is... life is like a movie where each character plays a specific part in the story of your life journey. Friends come and go but the truth also is that the true ones always stay no matter what, no matter how serious your fight was, no matter how big the distance is between you, true friends will always be there for you no matter what.

However, some people choose to ruin a friendship because of petty reasons, yes we all have problems but pushing your best friend away is a solution? Didn't know it was! If you truly are best friends, you wouldn't think or rather assume that one friend can hold back the other. Neither true friendship nor life is a rat race, there is no competition and that is something we forget as human beings, rather than looking at ourselves and working on our own lives we are always too busy envying others and commenting on what they have or don't have.

No two people, not even identical twins, are the same so how can two completely different people who are best friends be the same. Two people come together because they click, in some cases opposites attract. True friendship occurs when two people meet and say, 'Oh my, you too? I thought it was just me who did that or thought like that'. That is exactly when a truly beautiful friendship begins.

Having a beautiful friendship that is not only genuine but true and is filled with love and care between two friends is something that isn't very common these days. If you are lucky enough to have someone who is true to you, always has your back no matter what, someone you can rely on no matter what, then that right there is a true friendship. True friendship means being there for your friend even if they weren't there for you, it means having their back in front of someone knowing they're wrong but you don't do that to a strangers face, you can say whatever you like to your friend directly but never ridicule them to someone that isn't a part of your true friendship. Losing a true friendship isn't something you ever get over, especially if you considered that friend as a brother or a sister. Not many people understand this. Hope it was worth it for you!

CHAPTER 9: ABUSE

'The victim gets punished over and over...' – Rihanna.

Indeed she does, gets blamed and then punished. Why did she stay? Why did she go back? How could she be so stupid? Domestic violence is a choice that men make about the power and privilege they assume, and the way they use it. Yet so often it is framed as a choice the victim makes: that she chooses violence by not leaving, by falling in love, by giving him a second chance, by not wanting to be on her own.

Women go back because they feel like it is their responsibility to help the perpetrator; whether it's with his anger, insecurity or some underlying problem and that is the main reason we go back. We feel as if it our responsibility to fix him – a responsibility that every victim of domestic abuse is told by the world must be hers to bear. This is internalized by all women globally.

People may blame us for going back, for taking them back despite all the abuse, despite the long lasting damage men cause – but what they don't know is how difficult it is to let go. Yes, they hurt us, whether this is physical or verbal abuse – if you truly loved them, it is very difficult for a woman to just abandon the man she loves when she knows he's not all right. And most men aren't; I mean let's face it, would they really raise their hand on the woman they claim to love if they were sane? Would they really cause them to develop anxiety and have panic attacks due to verbally abusing them if they truly loved them? Would they blame her for his wrong actions towards her if he really was normal? No. No man who loves his woman would do that. And so being a woman, we feel it to be our responsibility to fix them, to help them... but often we forget that in fixing them, we are only damaging ourselves more than they have already done. It is not our job to fix them – we are neither behaviourists nor psychologists. Everyone in this world has their own role to play and we as women often forget that it is not our job to fix them. Our role is to walk away from them in order for them to realize that they have a problem that needs fixing.

I applaud Rihanna, not just for coming out with the truth but also for not feeling ashamed of being a victim to something so huge as domestic violence despite being a celebrity. I can guarantee you that if a man were to be in the same situation, he would not have been so brave. There is a reason God has given the responsibility of becoming a mother to women, because they are a brave species. If women want, they can do everything in life, if they were to put their mind to it. They are in no regards, less than any man. And this is something we as women often forget. I hope as our society is becoming more equal in regards to gender, more and more women will be able to come out and get the help that they need in order to deal with such a traumatising problem and feel free again.

Abuse – not all wounds are visible

When someone mentions abuse – the first thing that comes to mind is physical abuse, which refers to physical contact between two or more people that caused feelings of intimidation, pain, injury, fear, anxiety or any other physical suffering or bodily harm.

They say physical abuse causes wounds to the body that heal over time but verbal and emotional abuse causes irreparable wounds to the soul... wounds that can't be hidden unlike those on a person's body.

Research shows that 95% of physical abuse victims are women – but why is that so? Why is it that men think they can suppress women? Is it because they think they are physically stronger than us and hence can exercise their power? Why do these animals forget that they too came from a woman? I don't care what the books, cultural traditions or elders say – in humanity, it is wrong for a man to raise his hand to a woman. Truth is, men who do hit their women, wouldn't want the same for their daughters... so why then for their girlfriends, lovers or most importantly wives? Why the different rules?

Going through physical, emotional and verbal abuse changes you as a person, you are no longer what you used to be and this can be very difficult for anyone and everyone to understand, mostly for yourself. I mean if you can't understand it, then how can you expect someone else to understand what has happened to you and why you are a completely different person all of a sudden?

Most cases of physical abuse towards women come from those men that claim to love them... but truth is, that isn't love. Love doesn't teach anyone to be violent or cause any kind of pain, especially not physical pain to someone they claim to love. It is not the person they love but the power they have over that person, they love the control they can and do exercise over that person. And it is not that the woman is weak and hence, she allows it but more because she loves him and as mother nature has made us... we feel it our duty to care and look after others. As we love them so much, we identify that there this is a problem once the physical and verbal abuse begins and hence, take it upon ourselves to fix it. But we can't, we aren't psychologists and hence, end up being the victim to it all.

We are never able to fix our abusers, but in return end up damaging ourselves... the wounds from the physical abuse may fade but the picture never goes away... when they've grabbed your neck, pulled your hair, thrown you to the floor, slapped you to the ground and completely destroyed your soul. No one ever forgets that. As women, God might have made us strong and yes, we might move on with life but you never ever forget what that one man put you through.

The verbal abuse isn't any better; the control, the abuse, the swearing and the shouting, in some if not all cases can cause anxiety and panic attacks. For some who have never experienced such behaviour it can cause major health issues and that is exactly what happened in one case. It all started with loss of breath... leading to black outs... anxiety and panic attacks and ended with numerous incidents that ended up with the victim in hospital in a foreign country. That is the worst... being away from home, from parents, from friends and your loved ones and ending up in a hospital with your abuser alone.

People may not always understand or want to talk about it because not everyone does, in some cultures it is seen as taboo but this is the real world. People go through such experiences day in and day out with no one to talk to and that is the worst part.

If you know someone who has gone through any kind of abuse... you don't have to understand... just listen.

Blindness

There's no dearth of kindness in the world of ours; only in our blindness. We gather thorns for flowers.

Who would have thought two blind people would meet on an actual blind date? But they did, they met, she wasn't quite sure about it all and asked me to tell his aunty that he didn't like her but he couldn't, he fell in love with her the minute he sat down opposite her. He fell in love with her perfume, with her sweet voice, with the sound of her giggles and finally with everything about her once they did make a go of things and got together.

They were both blind but so perfect and happy. She played the piano at a dance school and he did voice overs for an anime company. They both still worked despite being blind, but of course it all sounds too good to be true. There were a bunch of gangsters who lived a few doors down from the happily married couple. One of them in particular, would tease the girl whenever she walked home and once when her husband witnessed this, he told them off and that's when things went wrong.

The next morning when the girl was home alone, the two gangsters went to her house and grabbed her... taking advantage of her blindness... covered her mouth and took her to the bedroom where they tied her to the bed and raped her. Both of them took turns. And they left her there... until her husband came home and found her tied up to the bed. He couldn't even hear her because they had tied her mouth too. It was all heart-breaking for the both of them. So much that it left her broken to the point where she wanted to end her own life.

They both went to the police but nothing happened. They gangsters weren't charged simply because one of them was the son of a major politician of the country. That's what the justice is for the rich and the injustice for the poor. It is sad to see that the people who can actually see and have eyes that can actually see couldn't see who did wrong, couldn't see the injustice being done to two innocent souls.

But that's life... human beings are awful beings. We often choose to see what we want and not what is actually true. This story shows that two literally blind people could see exactly what life is and how it should be lived, but those who aren't blind and can see the world chose to act blind in a situation where the injustice resulted to two blind people losing the happiness of a lifetime. That many that can see throw it away simply because they are not blind and can choose to see whatever they want with their eyes.

There's a story behind every smile

A smile I believe is the only curve that can put everything straight... but does it always?

What do we know about anyone's smile? Do you know the girl who has the most beautiful smile out of your friends is going through physical abuse by someone who claims to love her to the moon and back, but abuses her because she has a mind of her own and won't let him control her?

Do you know that the girl who wears her smile better than another one wears her diamonds is constantly being called 'fat' whereas she has the most gorgeous curvy body that every guy dies for... thick thighs... the perfect round ass and most importantly a beautiful, kind and loving heart.

Many of us wear a smile on our faces as truly and honestly as we can, but only we know the authenticity of that smile. Not many would know how many tears that smile has gone through all night before appearing first thing in the morning or how long it has had to struggle for in order to appear on your face for the world to believe. Those close to us often see the pain behind your smile and that is when you realize who your true friends are and who is actually there for you in reality, rather than just those people who we sometimes surround ourselves with either by choice or not.

There's been many times in life where I've been told I have a beautiful smile or asked how I manage to be so happy all the time and then there's those who often envy my giggles... but it's strange when I get complimented on my smile... rather than making me happy like it would any other normal person... it deeply saddens me because it's not real. It's not a real smile... mostly anyway... not many can see the tears in my eyes that are just waiting for my permission to roll out... but they haven't got that permission. But often there are situations where your eyes don't support your smile so what do you then? How do you make people believe in that smile that you're wearing because the truth is you're never fully dressed without a smile.

I remember being accused of being grumpy and ungrateful when a party was thrown for me and on that day the pain in my heart came across on my face despite wearing the biggest smile I could afford on that day... but how do I link the smile with my eyes? There's not a lot you can control in your body and that moment was exactly that. And sometimes sadly enough those around you who are supposed to be your loved ones don't always understand the pain behind your eyes or why the truthfulness behind your smile isn't linking with your eyes... and that hurts.

It's hard enough to wear a smile when deep down you're hurting like hell... but then to be accused but loved ones... kills even more. Be kind... there's enough horrible, selfish and self-absorbed people in this world... don't assume or judge anyone... leave that to God. Not every smile you see is real. Most of the time those with the most beautiful smiles have fought the toughest battles till date and have been through hell and back in order to be wearing that smile.

Out of sight... so out of mind and heart too?

They say you'll soon forget people or things that are no longer visible or present in your life.

Out of sight, out of mind refers to the idea that something or someone can easily be forgotten or dismissed as unimportant if it is not in our direct view. It's a funny saying because it's not always true... especially for someone rather than something. When someone is out of sight, it doesn't mean they don't mean anything to you anymore or that they're forgotten. Of course only if you're not actually trying to forget them.

The same goes for things... for me it was my phone... I had only had it for two very short months before someone stole it from me... right from my pocket. And the worse thing was I was already having a bad day.

My love was also stolen from me once... by someone who didn't actually know the meaning of love and that is what hurt. I always believe that when someone is out of sight, the only place they live is in your mind, constantly. Running through your mind... settling nicely in your heart that at times is the place they've broken into pieces. So even if they might be out of sight visually, they're not actually out of sight.

Having lived away from home on numerous occasions always made me think when they say 'out of sight, out of mind' do they really mean it? Does living away from home and from people who know you inside out mean that they've forgotten you once you're distant geographically? Is it just that easy to forget your best friend? Your niece who you spoke to every single day? The friend who helped you when your own family turned their back on you? How can people do that?

Distance, as I have experienced first-hand, not only shows you the true colours of everyone in your life but also exposes you to your true friends and their truth. At times this can be a nice surprise whereas other times it can hurt like hell knowing that those you'd do anything for don't remember you anymore or care about you anymore. For them you really have been out of sight and out of mind, but not only that in some cases you've also been out of their heart; either because you've been replaced or because of some misunderstandings caused by those who wanted exactly that.

Sometimes creating distance between people; whether intentionally or unintentionally will help people realize how much you actually mean to them. After all they do say distance makes the heart grow fonder. However, it does hurt when you realize that once you're back things aren't the same, people you did so much for in their time of need aren't actually there for you when you need them the most. Or have completely forgotten you...

But what I have learnt is that time reveals all so it's not just down to the distance. And we should be glad for the people who came into our lives as blessings and chose to stay rather than cry over the ones who came like a storm and caused only havoc.

Out of sight... doesn't always mean out of mind.

Live in the moment!

So many times you hear people say 'I can't wait for this or I can't wait for that, I can't wait to go on holiday or my first day at my new job or for the weekend'; I've done it myself... for a number of things or occasions or special moments and it is so bad because we are literally wishing our life away. Life is so short anyway and here we are wishing for a moment in the future to hurry up and come so that we can experience it sooner.

But then what about the time that we have now? What are we doing in that time? The moment that we are anxiously waiting for might be really special for us but what about the moments that we let slip out of our hands so easily? You do realize time never comes back.

There are many times I've heard people also say... 'I wish I could turn back time!' but the truth is you can't so why not make the present moment special, why not make it count? Too often I see people forget to live in the moment... they let time slip through their hands like sand does simply because they are waiting for another moment to come...

Live in the moment! Be happy! Live life to the fullest! Buy that gorgeous dress, or that X-box game, or that sexy Audi that looks hotter than your girlfriend! Who knows you may never get a chance again.

I know I've booked another big holiday to a complete different country after just returning from one simply because I can and I wanted to... I didn't know if I would live till next month or next year or the next time my bank balance was sufficient enough for me to do so. I had the time and enough money so why the hell not? As young people say... YOLO! Who knows if you'll wake up to the morning tomorrow. I certainly didn't know so I just went for it. At times the most spontaneous decisions are the best ones which then leave you with the most amazing memories of your lifetime!

My motto: Live each day like it's your last day on earth! And you'll never have a sad day in your entire life.

Love in Abuse... Really?

Love is many things, but it is never deceitful. Nothing toxic ever comes from true and genuine love, always remember that and don't let anyone let you think differently. A lot of people think that abuse in some relationships is part of love. 'He hits me because I deserve it or because he loves me and wants to reform my behaviour'. OR 'she hits me because she needs to get her anger out'.

Yes abuse isn't about a result of a males' actions, many women are known to abuse their male and female partners too due to various reasons. However, unlike women not a lot of men actually come forward due to the damage this can bring to their male ego, pride and masculinity.

The truth is there is no abuse in true unconditional love. Love is pure, while abuse is evil. Did you know one in four women experience domestic violence in their lifetime? That's one quarter of the entire female population in this world. And physical abuse isn't just a cultural or gender concept, it is more a vile human concept. People who have insecurity and control issues are usually the ones who abuse their partners, not because they don't love them but more because they don't have control over their emotions or actions, which then comes out in the form of built up aggression. I would say that I do feel quite sorry for such people but then again it isn't right for them to take this out on those they claim to love. And I understand that anger management is a real issue and a huge problem amongst many, but I absolute despise people that blame their anger for the actions of their fists or those kicks that they give the ones they claim to love.

Many women won't speak up against the men that abuse them only because they love them. I'm sorry but that isn't love, a person that can leave you blue and bruised doesn't love you. Love means feeling the hurt the minute you see or hear about your loved ones pain, no matter what you are doing or where you. Another reason why some stay in abusive relationships is because of loyalty. We feel disloyal for leaving our abusive partners because of their actions, as we may feel that their actions are out of their control and hence, indirectly it isn't their fault. However, that is very wrong. Never let your loyalty become slavery. If they don't appreciate what you bring to the table... then let them eat alone.

One thing we all need to understand as human beings and this goes for both, men and women is that we aren't God, nor do we have the powers he possesses. In short what I am trying to say is we can't fix people. Those who abuse in relationships, whether physical or verbal have some form of psychological issues which can be due to various reasons linking to their childhood, any abuse they may have experienced, their parents' marriage etc. but it is not down to us to fix them nor to help them through such issues. I mean if it was, wouldn't everyone be referred to as a psychologist?

There is a cycle in abuse whether it is the abuser or the victim. It is a very vicious cycle that just keeps going on until one person either ends up dead or decides to do the sensible thing and leave. But in no case whatsoever does love involve any kind of abuse; whether that's him grabbing your neck to the point where you can't breathe or hitting your head to the wall repetitively or kicking you in the stomach.

Love as the ancient Greeks called it was the 'madness of the gods', which according to modern psychologists is the strong desire for emotional union with another person.

Love is wanting to share the rest of your life with that one person who you want to wake up next to in the morning every single day, the one you don't mind giving the last slice of pizza to, the one who will see you at your worst with tears running down your face, messy hair drenched in rain but still call you beautiful, the woman who will stand by you no matter how bankrupt you go, the guy who will be there for you whilst you're dealing with pregnancy cravings for Ben and Jerry's at stupid o'clock. Nowhere in the world in any language or dictionary does love include abuse or any form of violence.

So please don't get the two mixed up – leave while you still can. It isn't your job to fix them.

CHAPTER 10: MILESTONES OF LIFE

There's nothing more attractive than a man on a mission...

Not everyone is lucky enough to realize what he or she had before it's lost... and that is exactly what he was... lucky. He had met an incredible girl, she was smart, ridiculously beautiful and ambitious; someone who knows exactly what she wants and most importantly what she deserves – there's nothing more attractive in a woman than this. As most boys are, he had been a jerk to her, taken her for granted, stood her up, not followed up on calls/texts – basically just been a typical immature guy who was enjoying trying out different flavours. But as life goes... when you meet *THE ONE* as they say, you just know, even the dimmest bulb in the batch knows or at least feels something – he did too, but was a bit too dumb or rather oblivious to what he was feeling.

He enjoyed talking to her; he could be himself around her he said with much relief; yet he didn't know why. It amazes me how oblivious some people can be to the feelings of others but most surprisingly to their own – and this is exactly when they lose the one they love or at times the one they need. The need to be loved, to be always needed by the one who loves you, to feel like you mean everything to someone, even if you mean nothing to the rest of the world.

When he finally met with the reality of his feelings for her and what she was – he went on a mission; a mission to give love a chance, with her. To win her over, to apologise for being an absolute immature jerk before and to finally tell her how he really felt. There is nothing more attractive in a man than when he is on a mission and knows exactly what he wants and will do anything 'to make her his'.

There were flowers; there was the truth, an apology, an honest outburst of true feelings and lots of cuddles. It was the perfect weekend, and one that was well spent. There's a reason women are teased to act like the FBI, we see through you guys, we know when it's real and when it'll last and when it's just fun and games.

This was real – the guy who had acted like an immature little boy had finally grown up, he knew what he wanted but also knew what he had to do to get it and that's what got him to his success – his love.

Not everyone is lucky enough to be loved back by the one they love, we live in a world full of selfish users who'll do anything and go to any extremes to get what they want and then walk away. So in a world where love has somehow gotten lost, it is always refreshing to see that still, there are some people that believe in the old fashioned, true kind of love.

The happiness... of a lifetime

It's true what they say... or at least she believed... love and death always come uninvited. And that is exactly what happened with her... she was broken, tired, frustrated and destroyed. She had been shattered by her first love, the one hope she had built her life around and once that hope broke... so did she... she stopped believing in love, in happiness and most importantly in happy ever after's.

And that's exactly when... love entered her life. Without her even knowing. They both worked in the same building of a corporate giant... just on different floors. One cold wintery day... when it was raining cats and dogs outside, with temperatures dropping by the minute and people worrying about leaving work as heavy snow was expected... there was a young woman in a gorgeous red pencil dress waiting in line at the Starbucks on the ground floor of her workplace. She was a head turner... not just because of her unique looks, but her style and the something she had about her that no one could ever put their finger on. She got to the counter and ordered her usual... "a mocha light Frappuccino please," and this time she didn't get the usual smile she gets but a huge shock as the cashier said... "ma'am... it's freezing today... you sure you want this cold?" and as always with a big smile on her face she replied, "yes please."

That was it right there... that big beautiful smile... that's where it all began... the most innocent pure smile he had ever seen and the cute little dimple on the side was just an added bonus. He was mesmerised by her choice... not of anything but her order. He had never known a girl to order an iced drink when the temperature outside was about turn icy. He knew just looking at her that there was something enchanting about her.

The next time they met was at the work vending machine where she was just wondering what to get; unaware at the fact that he was right beside her... waiting for her to finish but after five long minutes he made a cough sound, but to no avail. Not knowing what to do... he got close and spoke to her for the first time and that's where it all began. A friendship... they started meeting for lunches... going for coffee breaks... he had started ordering her Starbucks for her and got the funny looks from the barista instead of her. They'd wait for each other after work so they could walk to the subway station together. It was a beautiful blossoming love story. But a one-sided one... he was head over heels in love with this woman he had unexpectedly found in the least expected of places. And she was still the same broken girl... who had given up on love and on the idea of finding anyone... or of anyone finding her... but hey... isn't that where life surprises us?

He made moves... dropped hints but to no avail... it wasn't that she did it on purpose but she always was the kind to not assume someone's kindness was flirting. But he got anxious, as he wasn't getting any signs back. He even met her parents for

dinner one day and they all got along like a house on fire...
especially him and her mother. They teamed up against her.

Twelve months and 12 days into their friendship... he
decided to propose to her... he had the blessings of her
parents... the approval of her best friends and now it was
just hers that he needed. So closed up and guarded by walls...
yet so clear... like an open book... he knew everything about
her that mattered and what he didn't he wanted to learn
about her as his wife. He was warned about her painful
past but he didn't care. "Everyone has one," he said – "I know
she won't bring it in our marriage and if she does I'll help
her heal".

Much to everyone's expectations she said *NO* to the
proposal... but to everyone's shock... he wasn't disappointed...
he knew. I don't know how he knew but he did... he knew
she'd say no. He had gotten to know her inside out and he
knew that she had become this girl who thought she didn't
deserve love because she had let go of many guys that loved the
ground she walked on. She had something she was punishing
herself for. So Mr Clever Cloggs over here kept his real
proposal for later. After a huge discussion... a few tears, some
truths and promises... she agreed... deep down she knew he
would make her happy.

Hand in hand... her still a little nervous... he took her into a
dark room and then onto a few steps as if it were a stage... the
lights came on and she was standing on rose petals... her
favourite flowers... he was wearing a gorgeous navy blue suit
– one that she had picked for work for him when they went
shopping a few weeks ago and he was on one knee... proposing.
But he didn't ask her to marry him... but he asked her if she'd
allow him to be her bestest friend in the whole wide world, her
secret sharer, her go to person 24/7, her advisor, her cook, her
date for every date night for the next 100 years, the father
who'll spoilt her kids, the husband who'll love her so that no
pain can ever touch her and most importantly the Only person
who can make her believe in love again... ?

With a tear strolling down from those eyes... and a big smile with that cute dimple appearing that always made him go weak at the knees... but this time literally... she said, "Yes"... and before she could tell him to ask her parents for permission, the lights came on and they were all there. Family, friends, colleagues... each and every person that truly loved and cared about the couple was there to share their happiness and had watched the entire proposal behind the dark curtains.

A year-long engagement later they got married. She was promoted to a managerial position six months before her wedding, which was not only a dream come true but also one of her career aims. They bought a beautiful house together... with a rescue baby kitten for her and the most gorgeous puppy for him and then three years later a new member was added to their family. A beautiful little girl named Anna, a spitting image of her mother... the same curly hair... big bold eyes... magic to make anyone smile with those cute expressions and a tiny yet bossy little madam who knew how to put her baby brother in his place... even at that age. Two and a half years after their little princess they had a cute yet naughty little baby boy... and she finally got to name him Daniel... the name she had always dreamt of naming her son.

Then one day she stopped while sorting out meals for the kids... just to look at the reality in front of her... her unconditionally loving husband, her college best friend and two beautiful children all around her. She lost herself in this reality and kept smiling away until her best friend lightly smacked her around her head and said, "hey you, your smelly baby boy cleaned and changed... I can't believe that's the only reason I'm invited in this house."

And they giggled away just like she had always told her best friend that she would be on pamper duty whenever she had kids. She finally got her lifetime of happiness as her best friend had always told her she would and it was the best feeling in the world to be able to share it with her right there by her side.

Be ready at eight baby x

As soon as she got home, the doorbell rang again... she hadn't even had a chance to take off her coat. There was a man who looked like a delivery driver with a big rectangular box in his hands, wrapped up like a present.

She took the box and shut the door.

Upon opening the box, there laid a beautiful red dress (her favourite colour of course) with a note on top of the dress that said, 'Be ready at eight – there'll be a car outside waiting for you baby x'.

She loved surprises but didn't expect one from him, after all they had only been dating a few months and he wasn't exactly the romantic type. So all this was a bit of a surprise but nonetheless a pleasant one. There was a long black limousine waiting outside for her that drove her to a place where she had never been before... but she could see from a mile off because of the thousands of candles that had been lit everywhere. And as she got closer she saw a man in a black suit standing there... waiting for her... but wasn't facing her.

She got out of the car and started walking towards him, struggling, as she was never very fond of wearing high heels... as she got close behind him... he turned around just at the perfect moment as if it were all timed and gave her a bunch of red roses... her favourite. She always joked with him that she'd love roses while she's alive and lilies once she's dead.

Before she could even say anything he kissed her... softly but passionately... for what seemed like forever... he then took her hand and walked her to this deserted table under what seemed like a hut setting, where there was a candlelit dinner table set. He pulled out her chair like a gentleman and finally she could speak... she asked him what was going on and why he had done all this? It wasn't her birthday, or their anniversary or Valentine's Day... hence she was very confused.

He just smiled... and said that he doesn't need an occasion or a special day to treat his lady to dinner or to make her feel special. He thanked her for making every day of his life magical after coming into his life. She was ecstatic and could not believe him... after all she did have terrible luck with men in the past. But he was different; he was mature and sensible and had a good wise head on his shoulders. He knew what he had, which was special and a once in a lifetime kind of woman and did not want to lose her.

After they had dinner and talked for a while... he took her to the waterfront where there was an immaculate decoration of roses on the sides... after embracing her from the back while they enjoyed the view... he let go all of a sudden and she felt him disappear.

But when she turned around, she saw him, down, on one knee with an unbelievable diamond ring in his hand... and said those four special words, "Will you marry me?"

She was shocked... not sure in a good or bad way, then a big smile appeared on her face that lit up her whole face and made those eyes sparkle, which then within a seconds were filled with tears. She didn't say a word... and ran away from him while crying... leaving him confused and heartbroken.

Their day...

It was a beautiful spring day, birds chirping, butterflies floating around and flowers everywhere, after all she loved roses – her favourite flower.

He had filled her bedroom with flowers, mostly roses but other kinds too, there were tulips, daffodils, sunflowers and lots and lots of roses, of all colours – colours she had never seen before.

She woke up stretching her arms out and witnessed all the beautiful colours around her – he had got it all arranged for when she would wake up. There was also a special card for her that stated:

"Good Morning Beautiful...
Can't wait to see you...

Just relax... you will look incredible.
I should be worried...
Don't know how I will match up to you...
Can't wait to call you my wifey baby and...
Say I do x."

Her face was decorated with the biggest smile ever as she hugged the card alongside her teddy. She loved him... he was everything she wanted and most importantly needed; he knew how to calm her down, how to make her feel better and mainly how to make her feel loved.

As she started adorning herself, ready for the big day, there was more to come; he had left her small but so meaningful reminders of his love for her. The groom had arranged a stylist for her because he knew she would panic without one – she wanted to look extra perfect for him though he loved her just the way she was, but just to reduce her panic he got her some help.

As she sat down in front of the dressing table in her gown, allowing the stylist to take over, there was a knock on the door with someone bringing her some green tea and a piece of dark chocolate – he knew her so well, her routine, her likes, dislikes.

Without a doubt this thoughtful gesture made her smile – alongside the piece of dark chocolate was a note saying, 'I know you're smiling beautifully as you always do, can I please have a glance of that cute dimple – selfie?' To which she giggled and sent him one.

An hour later she was all ready, her hair in waves falling down her shoulders looking all lush, her dress fitting her so perfectly as if it were sown onto her and the minimalistic approach that she had taken with her jewellery and make up made her look natural as ever.

On the other hand, he looked dashing in his gorgeous dark navy blue suit that she had chosen for him, but he added a touch of her to it by choosing a subtle red tie to go with it – red because it was her favourite colour and every time he wore a red tie, it'd make her smile and so he had decided that he'd like her to have the biggest smile on her face when he asks her to be his.

He was very tender and cared about her to the core, she was very special to him and he was aware of this fact and hence, did his very best to always ensure she was content and smiling; after all it is that very smile that he fell for.

The way the couple looked just made the day even more beautiful. The ceremony was to take place at a boathouse – it was decorated with red lilies which are quite rare and that is what made it look unbelievable, her bridesmaids were in red dresses too which went perfectly with her gorgeous white dress. The groom's men were in smart black suits with navy blue ties to match the groom.

The flower girls and boys spread rose petals in the path that would lead her to the man of her dreams, the one she had waited for all her life – a path that she was about to walk down to never turn back – a path that was to change her life forever, one that would take away all the pain and replace it with just happiness and nothing else.

It was their wedding day and more than anyone the gorgeous couple was the happiest, with genuine beautiful smiles on their faces, immense never-ending love in their hearts and an eagerness to begin their lives together. It was the perfect wedding day filled with only happiness, love and lots of best wishes.

The Proposal...

She was in a gorgeous lace red dress... long locks falling down her broad shoulders... her body shaped like a guitar... curvy and very feminine – the dress outlined her curves perfectly. He was in a black suit with a white shirt bringing out his complexion... his hands locked in hers... hand in hand they both walked down to the river... admiring the stars that were lighting up the sky that night. They had spent the evening at one of his favourite restaurants at one of his favourite tables, which were nicely placed in one of the corners of the hexagon that the restaurant was arranged in. It was his favourite because of the setting, gorgeous wallpaper with unique lighting draping the walls around the table, but most of all because from where he was sitting all he could see was her and hence, it was his favourite table – he loved the way the lighting made her eyes sparkle and her cheeks glow – though he didn't realize that was more to do with him being with her than the lighting.

The pair had a lovely dinner; amazing food, interesting chatter, genuine laughter and her favourite dessert that he would always share with her despite having his own. Once they left the restaurant they went on this walk or should I say mission – it was his mission because she didn't know where it would lead to – he wouldn't tell her. This walk led them to one of the most beautiful and romantic places on this earth and most importantly one of her favourites – the Eiffel Tower in Paris. Yep, they were in the city of love.

She was shocked when she saw the Eiffel Tower twinkling with sparkly lights as it was on the hour – she couldn't believe her eyes and the happiness was clearly evident on her face that lit up and her eyes, which sparkled more than usual. Seeing her face glowing made him fall in love with her all over again. He couldn't stop staring at her face; the innocence combined with the genuine happiness made him go weak at his knees, which was ironic because within the next minute he dropped on his knees.

On his knees with a gorgeous yet very elegant ring in his hand and a big smile on his face yet nervously, he asked, "Will you be the one who completes me by marrying me and making me the luckiest man on this earth?"

Hearing this, seeing his face that depicted genuine emotion and his heart full of love for her, she smiled and said, "Yes".

Hearing the one word that would completely change his life forever made him ecstatic – he put the ring on her finger and took her in his arms and whispered, "Thank you baby, I love you".

This was by far one of the most romantic proposals ever – simple yet a very passionate and an intimate moment shared by two people who were bound by love to be together and complete each other.

CHAPTER 11: FRIENDSHIP

She's BAE

I don't even know where to start. She's not just my best friend, but more like the sister that I never had, but always longed for. There's always a reason why people come into your life and also one for why they leave.

My best friend came into my life to be my rock, my sister, my advisor, my partner in crime, my drinking buddy, my mummy number four to interrogate any guy I wanted to get involved with... basically to sum it up, my everything. And that is exactly what she is. As clichéd as it sounds I couldn't have asked for a better one. We met at college and though she's a year younger than me, we've both had life experiences shape us in a way where we're both way more mature than our age. I can't believe it's been eight years that we've been friends. I don't know how I've been able to handle you this long my dear and I guess you'd say the same about me – my crazy moments, times when I *LITERALLY* act like a little baby, the out of the blue giggles where you're waiting at least a good ten minutes to find out where that came from. I guess I'd be here hours on end if I listed everything we've done and experienced together.

But what I will say is that I really don't know where I'd be without you. You've been there through all the milestones of my life, through the graduations, through the breakdowns, through the celebrations, through the memorable nights and confessions and most of all the wrong boys.

We might not always agree on everything but we have learnt to agree to disagree and hence, we get along so well. Our friendship is really the truest of them all and I hope for the sake of both of us, it always remains that way – after all as I've told you before, you're on pamper changing duty for both of our kids, because Miss Business Woman over here cannot deal with that. And I'm warning you, no naughty stories about us in front of our kids... as the lord knows there are endless. Jokes part... as you've previously said and I've agreed, I do wish we live long enough and are best friends long enough to see our children play together and look at each other and laugh at how funny they are and then pass funny and rude remarks about each other... ending up in giggles, leaving our poor little ones confused as ever.

You'll always be my BAE though you do drive me crazy sometimes... or rather all the time and if you know any better... I'll always be yours. Can't wait to make many more memories together... laugh at many more nothings... go on plenty more adventures around the world and get through one hell of a journey called... LIFE.

Losing a friend

It's crazy how someone who used to be such a huge part of your life can be gone in a second. It's funny how exactly a year ago we stayed up until 3am talking and now I don't even know how to say hey'.

You were someone who became my best friend in a very short period of time... almost too quickly. But then again we were two peas in a pod, both crazy, spontaneous, adventurous, with not a care in the world. We could talk about absolutely anything without having to worry about what the other one would say – after all we didn't judge each other. We both had enough skeletons buried in our individual pasts and I guess that's what brought us together. After all pain does find pain in the end.

We were there for each other throughout the many ordeals life put us through whether it was to do with our families, with our individual friends or the different guys that came in and out of our lives. What I loved about us was that we loved each other so much that no guy ever would have been better for the other. You literally were a sister I never had... and always wanted. Hence, I trusted you with my life! You knew me better than my other best friend who had perhaps known me longer than you had... we shared secrets about anything and anyone... there were things only I told you. Some things that perhaps only you understood... even better than me.

You were my person! The person I could turn to with anything in my life whether it was a sorrow, happiness, a problem or an idea to cause trouble. After all we were known as the double trouble team. The things we did, the guys we teased and messed about with, the lectures we bunked, the movies we watched in a row, the songs we associated with and the numerous names we called each other. It was all just fun and games, a laugh – we were... just that... we were happiness for each other.

And hence, I never thought you would do this to me, just because two people are best friends, does not mean they'll have the same lives, the same happiness, the same success – we still were two very different individuals. And I guess that is exactly why I always wanted to see you happy, whereas you couldn't bear to see me. I never thought you would resent me for following my dreams and career aspirations. No wonder you didn't come to my graduation – you couldn't bear the thought of being there for me when I needed you the most that day just because we didn't graduate together. And that hurts.

There were times when things were good in your life and bad in mine but I never ever resented you for your happiness. It kills me inside to know that you resented me for going away from home for higher education – it didn't mean that I had left you, I missed you more than words can express... but what you don't understand is that if I hadn't gone away I would have ended up dead with everything going on in my life at that time. I needed to get away! But not from you hence, I always kept in touch, always checked up on you, made it a daily routine to talk every day. I was always there for you when you needed me the most but I can't say the same about you.

You were there for me when it was convenient for you, you even stuck your nose in my personal matters in regards to relationships but you really did take it too far when you ruined my relationship with my love. Someone who kept me alive while I was away... but little did I know he was my slow poison. I can't believe someone who is meant to be my best friend would betray me like this. You really have no idea of what you have done. You really don't. You didn't just ruin me but him too. You destroyed him and his belief in love. And most of all you lost me, your so-called elder sister that you were so scared of losing. Sometimes we lose the ones we are most scared of losing anyway as a result of our actions that we take to keep them.

I wish I could forgive you but I am sorry I can't, and the sad truth is neither can I forget what you did. I've tried and am still trying but I just can't. Thanks to you I'll never be able to make a friend a sister again and will think 100 times before caring to the extent I did for you for anyone else. You not only made him lose trust in love but you made me lose faith in friendship.

My sister from another mister... a bond of two loving hearts

In all honesty, my crazy, kind, silly and illiterate in mathematics sister is one of the main reasons I am alive today. She's been my rock! Through thick and thin, the ups and downs, the laughs, the unstoppable crying marathons and through every milestone in life. She's someone I can trust with anything in my life, absolutely anything; whether it's to do with family, other friends, career, education or even boys. The number of conversations we've had about the numerous assholes that have hurt us or at least attempted to! However, I do wish you had learnt some basic mathematics at least... God knows I tried when doing all your homework at school.

Though we've had our ups and downs too but still... 12 years later, we are still here. We're still solid as a rock, though we both live in different countries; we don't ever feel the distance because in our hearts we are still close. We might not be related by blood but I don't think that even if I had a blood sister, I wouldn't love her as much as I do my best friend... and I feel so blessed to have her in my life. I am so, so grateful to God for blessing with me with you... you mean the world to me... I love you the most and I can't wait to spend the rest of our lives just as we are... crazy, loving, loyal and most importantly as us.

It's funny when people say we look like sisters when they see us together, I guess it's because we love each other so much and when that happens... people do look similar... or so they say. But I don't think we do... you're so beautiful! I still remember the day we met... we had a test that you were preparing for and I came and sat with you and since then we have been inseparable. And I am so glad that I did. I know I left the country a year later but I mean look at us – the distance has not impacted our friendship in any way, shape or form. Yes of course, it would be nice to live closer but sometimes life shows us that if we get closer to our friends geographically, we get distanced from them through the hearts and relationships fall apart. After all there's a reason why they say, distance makes the heart grow fonder.

We're the same

It's not often you meet someone you connect with on a level... someone who understands how you're feeling and why you're feeling that way.

Someone who won't tell you that everything will be okay when you're going out of your mind with stress regarding life, work or people but will listen... someone who will actually listen to each and every word you have to say and allow you to let it all out rather than interrupting your feelings and disregarding your emotions.

I love how you believed in me at times where I completely lose hope and faith in my abilities and myself... I appreciate how you respect me like no one else ever has... for who I am... you recognize my capabilities and my successes and admire me for them rather than some people who would actually be jealous of them... it's amazing how similar we both are in regards to our ambitions and goals in life – how focused we are on them BUT without forgetting who we actually are as individuals.

Your work and writing are something you breathe in day in day out and that is what will make you successful, I love how determined and more importantly focused you are on what you want... I guess we both have that in common... but in all honesty... not sure if I've ever said this to you, but your determination really drives and motivates me when I need it the most.

You need to know this so get it into your thick head please – I really miss you when you're not here... I miss your wise words of wisdom, your belief in me and my capabilities and most importantly who and what you are to me – very special.

We met in a random and rather strange situation and special time in my life and I know you're going to laugh at me when I say this but I truly am glad that we met... there is definitely a reason and at times a blessing when certain people come into our lives and I guess you're exactly just that and I hope you're one that'll stay.

A best friend...

The best kind of friendships are fierce lady friendships where you aggressively believe in each other, defend each other, and think the other deserves the world. A best friend is less a friend but more a non-biological sibling – someone you can fight with, trust fully, share your naughty secrets with, act crazy with and someone who will always be there for you no matter what.

She is someone who believes in you when you yourself don't and can't believe that you are capable of getting through whatever it is you are going through. She will be there for you in times when you really need someone but are unable to ask for that help. She will make you smile in the darkest of times and make you cry with laughter with the funniest and dumbest jokes ever – but that is exactly what is written in her job description as a best friend.

A best friend is someone who will be there for you no matter what – even when you're being a complete dumb ass unreasonable bitch! Because that's exactly her job, to still be by your side even when you're in the wrong, because she'll make you see sense and help you get back on track. Best friends advise you like sisters and know when to smack you on the head too.

But what they don't do is betray you, lie to you, break your trust, or more importantly ruin your life. They be by your side no matter what is going on in their life or yours, they will always be there for you and help you get back on track.

I'm blessed to the max to have a best friend exactly like that; someone who is there for me no matter what. Someone who tells me off when I need it, will appreciate and encourage me when its most needed, will love me when I might not be so loveable to many and most of all will just love and accept me for who I am. Someone who will travel thousands of miles without even giving it a second thought just to see me and celebrate my birthday with me, someone who will talk to me until dawn about anything and nothing, someone who will get drunk way before me and zonk out, someone who will fight with me over the duvet and then over MY teddy. But most of all someone who will never break my trust or betray my love for our friendship x

Just remember if we get caught, you're deaf and I don't speak English.

Just Like Sisters...

They say you can choose your friends but not your family...
but this case was different... I chose for her to be my sister. We
literally were like sisters, I don't think I would have loved or
cared for my real sister as much as I did for her. We clicked
from the very first day – there was this instant understanding
and chemistry – the minute we spoke it was clear that we were
going to be double trouble together.

She was everything I wanted in a sister, someone who knew
how to have fun, cause trouble, make me smile when needed
it the most, but also to be wise and give advice when needed.
Be serious in situations that needed a more level-headed
approach and laugh our asses off in those that needed a few
giggles.

I can't even state the amount of trouble we caused together
along with the trouble we got into at home or with others
because of it. We were both like two free butterflies; we didn't
care about anyone else apart from each other. It was just we
two against the world. We were both there for each other
when no one else was – to hold each other's hand through
the storm, we danced together in the rain, wiped the tears off
each other faces and then went out and punched the asshole
who made the other one cry. Harassed the knob who made my
sister cry and made her go through hell. A sister is someone
who will tell you off for falling for a complete jackass, but
also be there after you did anyway and he's broke your heart.
A sister is there when he's beat you up or abused you despite
her telling you he's bad news, not someone who will taunt you
or throw it back in your face. An older sister is like a second
mother – just because mothers can't be everywhere, God
created sisters.

We weren't perfect, far from it but we were good, in fact
great, always there for each other, even when far, close to each
other's hearts. It was funny or shall I say I mostly found it
funny how we both knew exactly when the other one was

upset or feeling down or up to something dodgy or shall I say one of our usual shenanigans. But the truth is no matter how beautiful any relationship is, there are ups and downs, after all we are humans and hence, we had our fair share too, but the best thing was that no matter how far apart we went, we'd always find our way back to each other.

However, this time was different, things weren't the same anymore. One of us wasn't close to the other's heart anymore. We couldn't tell if the other was okay and that is exactly when a beautiful friendship of two sisters went downhill. There was no trust or compassion anymore. It was replaced by envy or rather guilt, guilt of weighing the other person down. Envy of having started together, but the other being ahead of you. At times we give ourselves up and let others make judgments for us and when that happens we lose ourselves. I guess in doing so we lost each other.

I would say not having siblings and then losing a sister is worse because it takes a lot to call someone your sister. It still hurts losing her because she wasn't only my best friend or just a sister, she was my very own baby sister – though only a year younger than me it felt more. I was very protective over her and a tiny bit possessive. We spoke all the time, day in day out. Spent whatever time we could with each other. Knew each other inside out or so I thought.

And then one day – I lost her – just like that.

Friend – A Special Person

A true friend is someone you can disagree with and still remain friends, if not, they weren't true friends in the first place. They are someone who is there for you when they'd rather be somewhere else. A friend is someone you can be yourself with, someone who you can have a laugh with at the time when all you want to do is cry, someone who is meant to be there for you no matter what, your three am buddy, someone you can force to watch your favourite TV show despite them absolutely despising it.

You're lucky if you have one true friend in life. Luckily I've had the opportunity to have more than one true friend in my life until now... but unfortunately not all of them are still a part of my life; which is something that makes me wonder if they were true. True friends don't abandon you when you need them most, in your hour of need. They don't betray you over a guy, whether it is someone they are involved with or someone you were with. They are the only person who is there for you when no one else in the world is, not even your parents or your siblings.

I had a best friend once, someone who I thought to be my true friend and someone I literally treated like my sister; especially because I never had a real one. I loved her to bits. I would have done anything to see her well, in good health and most of all happy. We were happy and the best of friends; so close that even my best friend before here didn't come close. We shared every single thing with each other, we laughed together, and we cried at the silliest of moments but regardless of everything were always there for each other until one day everything changed.

We weren't perfect but then again no one is, we had our ups and downs but we also always made up and smoothed things over. I am a huge believer of the old saying that everyone comes into your life either as a blessing or a lesson. This one was definitely a lesson. A lesson to not always trust so easily. A lesson to not always go out of my way for a so-called friend who wouldn't do the same for me. To not be so honest with a friend, because you never know when they can use that against you. Overall friends are amazing; true friends are your strength. They are your special people in this evil world that we live in, but not everyone who pretends to be your friend is a real one. A friend is meant to be a special person.

Choose yours carefully.

The LOC

There is a very fine line between friendship and love, the two most beautiful relationships that exist in this world that is filled with lust, betrayal and destruction.

In the small town of Malvern, there once lived two little kids, they were neighbours, a boy and a girl: Daniel and Anna. They became friends when Daniel found Anna sitting alone on top of a big suitcase up in the attic of her house. She looked adorable, such a tiny person on top of a long suitcase with fierce eyes looking at him and as he walked in she told him to come and sit next to her pointing with her little fingers.

He came and sat next to her on that suitcase, which was still huge even for the two of them, that exact moment is when their friendship began; an innocent relationship, one that grew as time went on.

They used to go to the same school and spent most of their time together; whether it was playing in the rain or pretending to do homework; from hiding from their parents to consoling each other when they fought. There was not a moment the pair didn't spend together; they loved each other before they were even old enough to understand the true meaning of love. But isn't that what true love is? Innocent, selfless and extremely caring.

They always looked out for each other, saved each other from their parents when grades didn't come as expected or when Anna broke the glass window while playing cricket or when Daniel forgot to do his own homework because he was too busy completing Anna's.

As time passed, Daniel realized his feelings for Anna were as a young man, but not a kid whereas Anna was very different. She didn't know how she felt about her own self and her scattered life let alone anyone else. She did deeply care about Daniel and loved him too, but was unaware of her own feelings for him simply because of the fact that she hadn't sorted out her life.

She had big plans, aspirations, dreams of being a rock star and all Daniel wanted was her. He was always there for her, through her song rehearsals, album launches and was still there when her album didn't do well. Call it bad timing but that was the day he proposed to her in front of her dad and his own parents and due to the huge audience, Anna had no choice but to say 'yes', despite not knowing whether she wanted to.

That night after everyone went to sleep, Anna sat by the window waiting for Daniel to come. And as he sat down, before she even said anything, he sensed something was wrong. He could see she wasn't happy. It wasn't something he had expected; after all she was the girl he had loved since he was eight years old. He had crossed the line of control between friendship and love a very long time ago.

She told her how she felt, that she hadn't dreamed of being just a wife and wanted to do more with her life but just wasn't quite sure what that was. She was a runner – someone who ran away every time things got tough. And that is exactly what she did the next morning. She ran away and moved to another city without saying a word. Often when there's not much to say or when we don't know what to say... we run away... whether it's running away from a situation... or most often yourself.

CHAPTER 12: RELATIONSHIPS

You've been messing around

You been messin' around – Enrique Iglesias

I heard from a friend who heard it from a friend
Who heard it from another that you been messin' around
I'm hoping that your friend, too, told you about me, too
'Cause I'mma tell you straight up, I been messin' around

Messin' around – what does it mean? Does it basically mean cheating?

You can be known to be messing around and that would be okay if you're single because it just means you're testing the field so to say... or keeping your options open... or recovering from a broken heart. Whereas if you do it while being in a relationship, that's when it's a problem... might not be for you but sure is for the one you're with. Though this doesn't stop us from doing it... does it?

A lot of people cheat in relationships... for many different reasons. I am not saying cheating or messing around in a relationship is right or justifiable, but at times the one cheating isn't themselves and hence, it shouldn't be taken personally unless and until it is personal and deliberate. I always believe if you don't like/love the person you are with, or don't fancy them anymore... it is best to break up with them rather than torture them by cheating on them and then breaking up with them later on.

However, sometimes people cheat; not because suddenly they've lost interest in the one they're with but solely because of underlying issues; issues that should have been resolved before they got in the relationship but that's not always how things work out. We don't always do what is right or what we feel we should do. Sometimes we just go with the flow, without acknowledging how we really feel or what we should really do. We all have baggage and it's never nice to bring that old baggage from a previous relationship into a new one because that is exactly when things go wrong. Sometimes we don't realize we're still hurting from what we've just been through and jump into a completely new adventure without healing... or fixing the damage we've been through.

Sometimes the one that we've cheated on may not understand why or how we could do it despite the love and care they have for us. At times they may hate us... abuse us with all sorts and may never forgive us. But truth is nothing they can say or do will make us feel worse than we already do. It's more difficult for someone who has cheated to forgive themselves for what they have done and the hurt they have caused their loved one than the person who has been cheated on. And that is what is hard; forgiving yourself, for being in a bad place. For not being able to deal with what we were going through at the time. For hurting so much that we had to turn to a complete stranger to forget that pain. That ache – for not being able to admit just how much we're hurting. But we are human at the end of it and it is humans that make mistakes. Forgive yourself. It's the only way.

Mr Player

Even a good player will someday become a toy of a better player. It's called karma. He wasn't good looking... rather a grubby looking guy with no real fashion sense... dark skinned with not a single good bone in his body. But somehow he still managed to get all the girls and even play them... something I never quite understood.

He claimed to have loved this one girl to bits... her name was Alina... he was with her on and off for a total of two years during which he cheated on her three times... sounds funny doesn't it? I mean why cheat on someone you claim to truly love? And most of all what did he get out of cheating on her? Some quick time fun with a random girl.

Even if sex means everything to guys... it can never compare to the love of a good woman, or the care she will give to the one she loves. Eventually she found out and broke up with him but it wasn't just a break up – he had broken her completely. Being cheated upon makes you lose not only yourself but your self-confidence as well and that is exactly what happened... she lost confidence in herself, in her appearance in what she did and most importantly in life. To get over the pain as most do... she started drinking, even smoking and sleeping around... exactly the way he used to do. Seeing this he was disgusted... did I mention he was one of those double standards kind of guys? If he does something, it is fine but if someone he knows does it... all hell breaks loose.

Oh well... after exactly a year from breaking not only Alina's heart, but the girl who truly loved him... he met another girl named Uma... who gave him exactly what he deserved. They say Karma is a bitch for a reason because truth is, it really is. She messed him around, played with his emotions, left him hanging while taking her own sweet time choosing between him and her ex, stringing him along – the same as he had done with a number of girls after which he broke their heart. Though karma got him... he never changed... after all once a player... always a player.

I don't get what he got out of playing with the emotions of many women... don't get me wrong... Casanova's appear cool but what's not cool is the damage they cause to genuine people who unfortunately enter their lives. Players feel the need to mess around with the opposite sex due to insecurities within themselves along with the need to feel wanted, to feel admired and desired, so to say. Hence, they constantly feel the need to play the field, see different people all at once because if they have a few girls on the go, they're never short of them. Whereas if they only have one girl in their life, there's always that fear of her leaving them.

Some people are born players but then there are those that are made into players due to them. If someone has ever dated/ loved a player and has actually been played/cheated by them will know what it does to them and how they go through a journey of loss, hurt, brokenness which then ends up with them converting into a player, just to see what the hype is all about, just to see why they were played and if there is an actual real reason behind it. And that is the saddest part – when you become the person that broke you. Being a player might look cool... but what's not cool is someone losing out in the game called life thanks to you being a player.

Being a father... was the best thing to happen to him

Being the only son definitely has a rather adverse effect on men, contributing towards their arrogance, over confidence as well as being spoilt by everyone, but especially their darling mother. And so was this guy. He would lie when playing with his sister that he was the one who won, he would get her into trouble with their mother for things she didn't do. And being a son's mother, she always believed her son... after all he was the apple of her eye.

However, most people believe children improve and stop misbehaving as they grow up and as time goes on, but that's not what happened with Isaac. One tiny thing that his mum said to him when he was five years old stuck with him like glue. When she told off his sister while playing, he got upset or pre-tended to be and that's when his mum asked him, "Who's the best? Who's the best?" But being the spoilt brat that he was he wouldn't respond and that's when she said, "Isaac's the best," which made him smile. And those three words stuck with him till he became a full grown adult. He would say them to himself whenever things didn't go his way or whenever he needed a tiny bit of confidence boost.

Isaac went on to being a very selfish, self-obsessed and arrogant individual who would only think about himself. His life was all about, 'Me, myself and I'. He never took into consideration the feelings of others, and not just strangers but especially the people close to him such as his live-in girlfriend of three years. For example, one day she asked him to pay for the milk, to which his reply was, "Why? I don't even drink milk". I guess he didn't really understand the meaning of living together or of having a relationship together. Or maybe he did not understand the meaning of a two-way relationship... because his mum had only taught him of one-way ones where his mum did everything for him without expecting anything in return and that is exactly where mums ruin their sons' upbringing.

He messed around, played up, broke promises, did not fulfil responsibilities and one day his girlfriend had enough. She realized that Isaac was never going to commit or grow-up and is a very selfish person. However, after three weeks post breaking up with him, she found out that she was pregnant with his child. She tried to tell him quite a few times but to no avail. He again played games with her, bringing random girls to their meeting place where she wanted to tell him that he was going to be a father. After numerous attempts, she left it, she didn't need him and if he wasn't ready to grow up, she decided he didn't deserve to know.

However, that's not how life works, a few months into the pregnancy Isaac did find out which left him broken because he saw it as a step back, he had moved on his life. However, the pregnancy not only woke him up, but his mother too who finally realized how wrongly she had raised her son, which was now causing another mother so much pain. She slapped him and told him to do the right thing because that is the only way she will be able to live in peace.

He was about to move to Paris with his new girlfriend because he genuinely cared for this girl, she was the one who removed his fears of commitment and almost made him into a new man. His career was going well... until the day he had a launch show when his ex-girlfriend went into labour. Much to everyone's surprise, Isaac left the launch to his colleagues and rushed her to the hospital where he discovered he now had another girl in his life... a beautiful daughter. Holding her in his arms almost changed him. It was a miracle. He promised to make her proud as her father. He didn't go to Paris but still stayed in a faithful relationship with his new girlfriend and was an amazing, caring and most importantly responsible father to his baby girl. While skype-ing with his girlfriend with his baby girl in his lap, she said, "You're the best baby... you really are... because you're the best thing to have happened to Isaac".

Isaac's unexpected new lady love changed him forever; she made him responsible for once and caring towards others and not just himself. And most importantly... she made him a good father.

Being a Father – Part 2

Being a father... is a choice... staying true to fatherhood is a duty. A father isn't defined as the man who makes the child by contributing his sperm, but rather the man who extends his hands and time to help with the child's upbringing and his heart to love the child through anything. Being related by blood doesn't make you a father, being a father comes from the heart. A father is someone who wants to catch you before you fall, someone who wants to pick you up, brush you off and let you try again.

He is someone who wants to keep you from making mistakes but also allows you to find your own way, even though his heart breaks in silence when you get hurt. A dad is someone who holds you when you cry, tells you off when you break the rules. He is also the one who shines with pride when you succeed and will always have faith in you even when you fail. He is the one who holds your hand and teaches you to walk, not just physically but also on this journey we call life.

A father is the only man who will warn you off all other men, teach you how men really think, test out any boys that show an interest in you, are critical of any boyfriends that you may have... and yes, the truth is that no prince will be good enough for your father, the king.

The father doesn't always have to be the typical breadwinner in the family , but he has to know how to be there for his daughters and not just be this man who is close with his sons because he is the only person who can teach them manly things. There are mothers who play football with their sons and father who are there for their daughters, father who run to the store to buy them pads or tampons, fathers who question their daughters about the guy from school who walks them home, or the one who dropped them off at home after work. Fathers who care not just for their daughter, but for their wellbeing and most of all their happiness.

A father is meant to be the best friend a son can have, someone who will teach them how to play football, how to ride a bike and drive a car, someone who will give them advice when they start dating, give them an insight about what to expect when they hit puberty, and finally someone who will teach them not only how to be a good human being, but most importantly on how to be a gentleman and be true to yourself and to always, no matter what, treat a woman right.

With a daughter, it is important that a father is there for her, sets a good example of what to expect from a man by treating her mum right and always being there for her. A father is a daughter's king and it is only by his example will she base her selection for her own prince. It is important for a father to reassure his daughter, but also prove that he is always there for her and that she can turn to him no matter what. To inform her of what men can be like and when to walk away from the things that no woman should tolerate from a man such as abuse and cheating. In many cultures, daughters can't turn to their fathers or even both parents because of a barrier between the two, which is given the name of respect, which isn't actually respect.

It is important parents know what is going on in the lives of their children and this goes for both parents and both genders. Sons need the same attention that daughters do, most people focus on making their daughters good women and forget to focus on their sons just because they're men? What they forget is that in doing that they are allowing their daughters and many other girls to fall for men like their sons who haven't been brought up in the right manner, not been shown how to treat a lady or how to respect her. In making your daughters good, sensible and pure women, you forget to focus on the sons who then grow up to be animals who take away the purity and innocence of many women such as your daughters.

Being a father and a parent means being there for your child at all times but especially at times when they need you the most. Identifying when things don't seem normal, when your child is upset or more quiet than usual. When there are abnormalities in their behaviour. Supporting them when they make mistakes and encouraging them to try again after learning from those mistakes. Motivating them to better themselves when they've got a B in exams and not an A, when they're wanting to go for a career change or a new job. Appreciating their efforts whether it be a few kind words or a bunch of flowers that just shouts out, 'Well done'!

When you're gone all your kids will remember are the best times of their life that they shared with you, those special occasions such as exams, graduations, birthdays, festivals and their wedding day when you were always there, where you went above and beyond to make their day special and most importantly to make them smile.

Contributing your sperm during sex doesn't make you a father, taking responsibility, being there for a human that you have helped create and giving them the love, care and affection is what being a father is all about. And sadly often many people forget this because of life getting in the way but that's just an excuse, nothing can get in the way or being a father because in all honesty it is one of the most beautiful relationships any man will ever experience; only if done right.

Why stay in a marriage?

In almost all religions, marriage as seen as the utmost sacred bond between two people, two people that vow to love, cherish, protect each other until 'death do us part'. I believe that the vows that you make to each other on your wedding day in front of God the Almighty, your family, friends and loved ones are most important in those moments when they are most difficult to keep. And that is the true test of your marriage and can raise questions in some marriages for either partner, as to 'why are they staying?'

In the olden days, some like to believe we lived in a very male dominant society and if a woman were to leave her husband it meant she didn't have anything and lost it all. Not true. There are many others that have gone against this stereotype, left their husbands, even experience being banished by their own flesh and blood, their parents, with nowhere to go but still made it in life. These are the strong women who made it in the evil world we live in where a woman has to go through tests and obstacles at every step in life; but still come out stronger; they raised their kids without the help of a so-called man (their husband) and raised them well. Because the truth of life is that a mother can be both, a mom and a dad whereas a father no matter how hard he tries, can never replace a mother, the maternal instinct or motherly love. After all there is a reason God chose the mother to be a child bearer rather than the male.

But for the sake of that child would you stay in an unhappy marriage? In a marriage where you feel more alone than when you were single and unmarried? Where your husband doesn't support anything that you do simply, because he is a waste of space, an insecure, easily influenced weak man who couldn't do anything in life and hence, has chosen the easy way out to lead a life of misery. Would you? I know women who would say yes to this question without a doubt, simple because of SOCIETY.

But let me ask you... will society care when your child is witnessing your husband arguing with you over nothing, shouting at you, putting you down, simply because he is insecure, stubborn and cannot provide for his family? Will society care when your child grows up not to believe in the institution of marriage? Will society be there to wipe the tears off of your child's face when she lets a man treat her like dirt, because that is exactly how she saw her father treat her mother? The answer is a big fat NO.

At the end of the day we were made by God and to Him alone we shall return. I agree we live in a society in this temporary world, but the gossip kings and queens will talk about something you did that they don't agree with for a day or two and then will go back to their sad old lives, but YOU are the one who has to deal with the nonsense and utter bullshit that your husband or wife puts you through... so why stay?

The world knows there are millions of single mums who have done an amazing job raising their kids so why can it not be you? Especially when most mums have to do the job of both parents anyway in cases of lousy fathers? Seriously why?

Every human being, especially every woman deserves happiness. Your wedding day is supposed to be the best day of your life and marriage plays a huge part in making that life happy, so why stay in an unhappy marriage? Yes it hurts leaving, failing a relationship but does it not hurt more when you are made aware of the fact that you failed every single day?

Most stupid and imbecilic women think it would be better to stay in an unhappy marriage for the sake of their children, well let me enlighten the dumb shits, your kids are worse off in an unhappy marriage because you're showing and most importantly teaching them the wrong concept of marriage but allowing yourself to be treated badly. Most women that tolerate domestic abuse do so because they've come from parents that did not treat each other the right way – think of it this way... why would your child want to even get married when they are older if they've seen what a miserable marriage you've had. After all it begins at home, the environment that you've grown up in is what shapes you.

If you've done everything to save your marriage but nothing has worked, simply walk out because you and your children deserve better. If it's meant to be, not even God can stop it but if not, not even He can save what you may call a marriage but is actually a disaster.

A Life Partner...

A life partner is someone who is your other half, someone you want to share your entire life with, a life-long best friend who slowly becomes a part of you. Time decides who you meet in life, your heart decides who you want in your life, and your behaviour decides who stays in your life. Choosing a life partner is a huge decision because this is someone you will be spending the rest of your life with, someone you will share all your secrets with, this person will be someone who you open up to like no other and you want to make sure that this is the right one.

I don't believe in the term divorce, hence choosing the right life partner is something I believe is very important and a very tough decision. You don't just choose a life partner because you have to get married or because you should get married as you are coming to that age, but because you are now ready to share your life with someone else, you feel comfortable with yourself and with where you are with your life now and are willing to let someone else enter it and share it with you.

Choosing a life partner is huge but choosing the right one is even bigger because it is important that you choose someone who will be able to share your life with you and vice versa, someone who will help you become a better person but also accept you for who you are, someone who won't make you change yourself just because they think you're a little under or overweight. A life partner is someone who sees every side of us so it is important for us to feel comfortable with them, someone we feel safe with and most importantly someone we won't mind showing our most vulnerable side to.

A life partner is someone who sees you not only at your best, but also at your absolute worst and this person still has to be able to love you, be there for you and always be by your side on both extreme poles. It is vital that your life partner is there for you during the storm and not just there when it's time to dance happily in the rain.

We see many relationships where only one party makes all the sacrifices, and this can be both men and women and that is exactly what we should not aspire to be and have. It is important that in a relationship both parties play an equal part. The man should not have the power over the woman to tell her what she can and can't do and the same goes for women over men. Being in a relationship of marriage is NOT about power and control but rather about love and companionship.

You are blessed if you have a life partner who loves and respects you, because at the end of the day that is all that matters. You want someone who you can see as a mother/father in for your future kids, someone who will treat your parents as their own and someone who will not only be your life partner but your best friend and partner in crime. This is the person you will want to share everything in your life with, someone you will look up to for everything, someone who will always push you to achieve your dreams and goals and will support you 100% while you do so. Someone who will love you even at the times when you are least loveable.

A Life Partner is someone who doesn't complete you because you should feel complete within yourself but someone who adds value to your already amazing life and makes it even more exciting and worth living and more adventurous – so choose wisely – listen to your heart but also take your mind's advice. After all they are both important.

I Won't Give Up

I Won't Give Up by Jason Mraz – One of the most beautiful songs ever written

I'm not an expert at relationships. I don't know how to handle every fight we're going to have, and I will never be a perfect person. We're both still young, and we still have a lot more to learn. But I'm willing to take chances, to risk it all, and learn everything there is to know just so I can keep us together. I won't give up on you. Most couples that are 60 years old and over and are still together can only give us youngsters today the advice that is the key to having a successful relationship, which is to fix things and not give up. Because the truth is today's generation looks at throwing away a relationship at the very first hurdle or difficulty but that's not how love and relationships work.

It's kinda like baking a lasagne... you won't complete it unless you put in all the layers and just like that you can't build a relationship if you don't put in layers of love, trust, honesty, care and forgiveness – you won't get there.

Same goes for an exam, if you don't study and work hard and just give up because the content seems too hard – you won't achieve what you had set out to gain in the very beginning. Hence, giving up isn't an option and those that gave up didn't really want to achieve their goal anyway, because if you really want something, you never give up – you do your best to gain it whether it takes a lot of hard work, consistency or forgiveness – You Never Give Up. In life, there are many moments where you might feel like giving up and I don't blame you because it's easy isn't it, just giving up and not trying anymore because it is a lot easier than carrying on and pushing yourself to achieve that goal you had set yourself before things got tough?

Giving up on your dreams isn't just giving up on them but also letting go of all the aspirations that you had linked with those dreams. Unrealized dreams and defeated expectations hurt a lot more than not achieving what you want the first time and just giving up.

On the other hand, giving up on a relationship is a lot easier than working towards it and building it to be something beautiful and life lasting. And that is the main problem with today's generation – if something breaks we feel like it's time to throw it away but that isn't how things work – if something broke back in the day, people tried their very best to fix it and that is why today we see couples in their late 60s and 70s with perfectly happy, healthy and love-filled relationships. It's not because they didn't have fights, or arguments or hated the other persons guts at one point or another but because their love and willingness to make it work was a lot bigger than their ego and their hurt. Quite often we hear that we only get angry and end up hurting the ones we love the most and we do, but we should also have the courage to apologise when in the wrong, know when to put things right and always respect and love each other in order to keep things going.

I won't give up on us... even if the skies get rough... I'm giving you all my love... I'm still looking up.

Distance...

Distance... the length of space between two points or the gap between two physical locations or two people based in two different locations. It can be positive and negative, it can prove to work out for you as well as work against you.

The main thing about distance is that it sometimes lets you know who's worth keeping and who's worth letting go; because the truth is that those that matter don't care about distance and those close to your heart will never ever be able to create a distance between hearts.

Loving hearts will still love each other no matter what or how much the distance is between them... geographically or emotionally. There are many long-distance relationships that work only because people don't give up on each other. Every relationship goes through some form of distance at one stage or another but the key is not to let that distance get in the way of that relationship and of your happiness.

Distance in families is another major issue; there are some that have distance between them caused by fights that have led to family members drifting apart; whether it be parents, siblings or even the extended family. And this gap just gets bigger due to a lack of communication, which then eliminates the love that held the family members together for so long in the first place.

Then there is the distance where someone is away from you by sight for a short or long period and time shows how that has or will have an impact on your relationship. Having lived away from home for so long has definitely helped me understand the value of distance and how it shows you the true colours of some people. There are those that no matter what or where you are will always be close to your heart and then there are those that are just waiting for distance to use it as an excuse for not being there for you or letting you down.

I actually have a best friend with whom I have a very long-distance relationship to the point where we don't see each other for years, but whenever we do talk or see each other, nothing has changed, we pick up where we had left off... and that is the beauty of relationships that are based on pure love. Distance – it gives us a reason to love harder. The truth about distance is that it means so little when someone means so much.

The 3P's – Parents, Pedestal, Perfect

Because of the pedestal we put our parents on and the importance we give them, we often forget that they too are human beings just like you and me and hence, can also make mistakes.

Because the truth is parents make more mistakes than their children and it's only because it's all new for them as well – they didn't know how to raise children when we first came along and funnily enough we didn't come with an instruction manual either. And let's be real – none of us have been an easy ride to have.

First of all our parents have a generation gap between them and us, hence; there's a huge different in values, beliefs and most importantly mind-sets, simply because we both don't think or feel the same way. For example, something we may wear today may be totally cool for us and we may not see anything wrong with it but on the other hand, for our parents that may be a completely different story – for them our dress code may be totally unacceptable and shameful in some cases.

On the other hand, our independence; something our parents will never understand and hence, I've given up; is something unique to our generation and perhaps our parents letting us down and not being there for us has played a huge part in that. I know it has for me and it's not a dig but a revelation that parents can't always be there for us when we need them, yes they should but like I said, they're humans too.

Another important revelation, perhaps something I knew but just never acknowledged was that parents make mistakes, their mistakes which at times can ruin the lives of their children emotionally and psychologically and it always amazed me how a parent can firstly let that happen and secondly not realize that? But recently through a psychologists seminar I realized how they can. In their generation seeing psychologists or going for therapy wasn't the norm. Despite some kids having doctors for parents, counselling for their generation was always seen as a taboo. And that is perfectly fine, after all you can't expect someone who is completely new to your generation and your life and mind-set to understand how you feel.

They fail to understand that the way we go to a General Practitioner for issues with our body, we can go to a psychologist for issues with our brain. It makes me laugh to think that parents don't realize that the brain is also a part of our body and if there is a problem we can easily fix that too, just like any other diseases; a cold, lung disease or jaundice.

Being let down by parents and them causing you hurt that you don't think you'd ever recover from can kill, in fact destroy a child's soul, but just like forgiving anyone else, a friend, family member or lover, we owe it to them and more to ourselves to forgive them, to let the pain go, to let the disappointment go because if we don't it'll consume us and that is not something we want.

So if you've ever been let down by a parent before, go up to them and forgive them, yes it'll hurt if they acknowledge they've done it but remember you're not doing it for them, but for yourself. Let that pain go. Let that disappointment go, start believing again and remember our parents are humans too and hence, can also make mistakes just like the rest of us.

Come back to life! Say hi to life again because truth is you probably haven't in a very long time.

Marriage – A little compromise, A little sacrifice...

Very rightly said, marriage is about becoming a team. You're going to spend the rest of your life learning about each other, and every now and then, things blow up. But the beauty of marriage is that if you picked the right person and you both love each other, you'll always figure out a way to get through it
– Nicholas Sparks.

A marriage... is one of the most beautiful relationships between two human beings after that between a mother and a child. A child might leave their parents' nest once they are 16 or over or when they turn into adults; but a husband and wife that are true to each other and purely love each other can never leave each other's side until death do them part. Marriage is the purest bond between a male and a female, a bond that links them together for life; a life full of ups and downs, happiness and sorrow, sunshine and dark clouds, brightness and darkness.

No marriage in this world is ever perfect, because no two people are perfect. When two people alike or different come together there is a lot of change for both of them, a lot of adjusting to do, forgiveness to give and a lot of second chances to give, but no matter what you don't give up. Two people that truly love each other will always make their marriage work no matter how difficult it gets; it can be financial issues, being infertile, being addicted to drugs, alcohol or sex, one of the two being jobless, families dispute and God knows what not.

But in any healthy relationship, there is no difficulty that two people in love cannot overcome if they truly want to. There is a reason why in almost all religions marriage is seen as one of the purest forms of love. There is a reason why sex before marriage is seen as a taboo, it is because marriage is the only relationship that joins two people in love in a bond unbreakable and pure. A bond that allows two people in love to officialise and legalise their relationship and gives them a name that they can be known by in the world.

In Islam, it is very beautifully put that they (your wives) are your garments and you are a garment for them. Islam enjoins that a wife and husband should have the most intimate and loving relationship. Each should cover, protect, and safeguard the interests of the... other partner. And that is exactly what a marriage is about... a little bit of compromise on both sides and a little sacrifice in order to let the relationship blossom and bloom.

There wasn't anything amiss in you... it was me

It's not you...it's me. The typical line someone says when they want to break up with you when they either don't want to tell you the real reason or don't have a solid reason to give you. For me that wasn't the case... there genuinely was nothing wrong with her... it really was me. I was the one who was missing all the qualities that someone she deserves should have.

She was this stunning, naturally beautiful and fun-loving girl, someone who was so easy to get along with; enjoyable to spend time with and someone who was literally unbelievable. I have to admit I was quite nervous to meet her for the first time when our parents had set us up, but as cheesy as it sounds, she had me the minute she blushed, following it with a smile as innocent as that of a baby.

Much to my surprise our conversation flowed freely and we got along like a house on fire. I told her all about me and she shared a lot about herself. We were similar in more ways than one and that was jaw dropping; I had never gotten along with someone as easily as I did with her.

The more time I spent with her, the more I realized just how much I liked her and how shockingly different she was from the girl who had betrayed and broken me to the point where I didn't trust women anymore. My so called first love, the girl I lost my virginity to and the one I had dreamed of marrying someday, the one who made me want to better myself and succeed in life. Little did I know all she wanted was my money to maintain a luxurious lifestyle but as all other men when in love, I was too blind to see that.

The day I resigned from a job that I was unhappy with, she left me because I was jobless... it sounds funny when I say it now, but it wasn't at the time; it broke me. I had to leave a job I loved because there were issues with my boss that I couldn't solve, despite trying so hard for so long. But that wasn't all; her leaving me completely broke me. I stopped believing in love, in women and in some way in all mankind. I even stopped loving my mother for a while simply because she was a woman and perhaps, also because she was trying to help me get over her and come back to life.

When I told her all this, despite being scared that she might leave me, I was shocked to see how understanding this girl was, so smart, wise and a very practical young woman who dealt with situations very realistically. She was sympathetic but also admired my honesty for telling her about my past. Funnily enough, we had another similarity, she too had been heartbroken by someone she truly loved and much to my amazement, understood me way more than my own mother ever did.

On our next date I thought to myself, 'Gosh, this girl is full of surprises,' you wouldn't believe but she didn't let me pay for her, for our meal or for our river cruise. I was shocked, I was used to paying for my ex, with everything. She literally lived off of me. And now that isn't in my life, it all makes sense. She really was with me for my money.

But this girl, she was different, she was independent, she even told me as a joke that she didn't want a guy who can pay for her but rather someone who can be there to carry her bags, as she was a shopaholic. That is something that really touched my heart; it was almost refreshing to actually meet a girl who didn't want anything from me.

But knowing all this made me worry; made me nervous almost. I started feeling insecure. How could someone who was younger than me and had been destroyed a lot longer than I had by someone we loved be so normal? How could she sympathize with me and give me hope despite being broken herself? Like how?

Despite having been through hell and back at such a young age, she still was so intact or at least she appeared to be. She was still hopeful, she was even willing to give love another chance despite having been broken for a lot longer than I had. Being a man, I felt so inferior to her. I felt as though I should have been the one who was being strong and more level-headed in life... but I wasn't. I was completely broken. I wasn't even hopeful about my ACCA exam, nor my job. But despite not knowing me well, she gave me hope and told me to be positive in life and that I would do well based on my efforts.

She made me want to do well in life not just for myself but for her. I wanted to marry her and with marriage comes responsibility. I had always seen my dad take full responsibility of running the house and keeping our family financially stable and so the idea of a woman who didn't need that from me was a bit bizarre but the problem was I felt like I wasn't good enough for her because I didn't have a house nor was I settled or stable in my career of life and that scared me.

There really wasn't anything amiss in her. She was nearly perfect and I couldn't wait to start a life with her because I knew she would make me the happiest man on this earth. She was sensitive, considerate, caring and someone with a huge heart filled with kindness and generosity. And me... I was nothing compared to her. I didn't have a good relationship with my parents or siblings and didn't have many friends either. I actually considered myself as a failure and she didn't deserve that; she deserved more... a lot more.

So yes... there wasn't anything amiss in her... it was me.

Before you assume just anything about anyone...

Making assumptions about someone simply means
believing things are a certain way with little or no
evidence that shows that you are correct; and you can
see at once how this can lead to terrible trouble
– Lemony Snicket.

It's just so easy to make assumptions about other people, their actions and most importantly their lives – without even knowing the full story or even asking them about anything. Sometimes we think we know people so well that we believe the assumptions we make about them. For example, it is so easy to blame a teenage bully for their actions and their behaviour towards their peers at school. But do we ever think why they have resorted to bullying? Perhaps they are a victim of verbal abuse by their parents or carers or even worse, they themselves might be being bullied by their own siblings and hence, bullying others at school might be their only way to lash out at someone.

That woman who covers herself in foundation on a daily basis doesn't do it because she is obsessed with make-up but because she wants to cover up her bruises because she has an abusive husband who beats her black and blue every night after he gets drunk. Why doesn't she leave him? Is the question on your mind right now right? Did you know he threatens to harm their first born if she leaves him? Do you know her mum is a heart patient and if she found out that her only daughter is with an abusive man it would kill her.

Intense stuff right? Exactly! Don't start pointing fingers at people if you don't know their story. Ever wondered why that extremely good looking guy at work is seen talking to a different girl every day, ever wondered why he stopped dating you despite you guys having an amazing concoction. No guy is born a player but rather he is made into one.

Did you know he has a phobia of being left? His mother abandoned him when he was six years old, just old enough to understand that yes his mother did leave him; when he was still a little child. To top it off his dad told him that she left because of him. You can't even imagine how that little boy must have felt hearing those words and on top of that having to live with that for the rest of his life. No wonder he has commitment issues. He thinks if he gets close to a woman she'll leave him and that is why he leaves you or dumps you the moment he realizes he is getting attached to you.

Yes alcohol, drugs and suicide aren't solutions for shitty lives but have you ever wondered how bad someone must have it for them to go through all this. For them to end up at death's door. We hear people talk about insomnia, but you can't imagine how someone must feel when they've not slept more than 20 minutes a night, when despite not wanting to, the only way they can have a good night's sleep is drinking alcohol. When someone is so numb that self-harming themselves is the only way they can feel anything in their body. When the pain gets so much for someone that the only escape for them is taking drugs and even if for a short while – getting away from that pain.

The people with the deepest pains and scars often wear the brightest and most beautiful smiles. They are the ones known to be a ray of sunshine despite the storm going on deep inside them. At times those that are always there for you don't ever have people who are there for them. There's a reason they say don't judge a book by its cover. There are people fighting battles worse than in the war zone, which you know nothing about. Always be kind. Don't judge nor assume. But listen.

CHAPTER 13: THE MALE SPECIES

I broke her...

She was gorgeous, a pretty fashionista, looking beautiful and smart even in a uniform as boring as ours... there was something about her I felt the minute I set eyes on her. Not a lot of women have that something sexy about them whilst still displaying innocence on their face that makes them shine bright like a diamond – but she did. I knew from the minute I saw her smile that I had some sort form of attraction towards her... I kept hovering around her without her even noticing me until I finally had to go and introduce myself because damn, this girl didn't set her eyes on me.

Love at first sight – something I used to laugh at and make fun of, but it is true because it happened to me... or should I say us. There was this chemistry and attraction between us from the time we spoke for the first time till... today I guess, that just never went away no matter what happened between us.

She loved me and I broke her... looking back I feel like a complete asshole... it was me who approached her, before then she didn't even know I existed. There were sparks between us which I know we both felt, but the fact that I knew that then perhaps made it easy for me to mess her around.

I still remember her smile, the way she looked at me... later on how she started caring about me... and I just threw all that away... I threw back her love in her face... her love for me scares me and perhaps did back then too. As a guy we mess up mostly when we know we've found the one and that is exactly what I did. I remember the day years later when I told her, "You know not even my wife will love me as much as you have". And I could see her look away because I knew she was going to cry.

Her strength and perseverance astonished me back then and still does, that girl never let go, not of me and not of the hope that we will end up together. I was surprised she wanted to be with someone like me, someone who messed her around, strung her along. I guess I did that because she felt like 'the one', she was my safety cushion and I just couldn't let her go. There were many times that she told me to let her go but I couldn't, I knew I wouldn't be with her but despite knowing the truth I just couldn't let her go. For some reason I always wanted her in my life and if truth be told, I still do.

We've spent ten years in each other's lives, as twisted as it sounds, I always enjoyed having her around in my life, she was the only person I could talk to no matter what was going on because she never judged me, she wasn't like that, you see she was this unbelievable person with humane qualities. An absolute selfless and genuine character who didn't give up or let go no matter what I did or how badly I treated her and looking back, it wasn't bad... it was despicable.

A decade later... now that we're all grown up and leading very different lives, it scares me... my treatment of her scares me, karma scares me. I broke the one girl who loved me deeply and unconditionally and it scares me to think what if it all catches up with me? What if I end up with someone who treats me the way I treated her? What if I end up with someone who doesn't love me? Or the worst of all, what if I end up with someone who plays me just the way I did her?

Years later now when I'm a little mature or at least I think I am, I've realized what I did – I broke the only girl who loved me and ever will, because in all honesty I don't think my wife will love me the way she did. I've seen her change over the years, become stronger, portraying her innocence less obviously now, it kills me to see this every time, but I can never tell her it is the wall she now has built around herself... and I don't think even I can break that.

But what I also do know is that she will love again... maybe not soon, but eventually she will because she will end up with someone who will adore her the way I never did, never ignore her the way I always did, not break her but build her the way I never did and most of all make her realize that she is one hell of a lady who is not only very special, but the most kind, genuine and truly loving woman – someone not just any man will be lucky to have but the right one will be exceptionally lucky to have her in his arms. A decade later, I wish I could go back, but I can't because she doesn't deserve to be reminded of all the melancholy I have caused her over the years or how I broke her bit by bit.

Sitting in your T-shirt...

Sitting here in your T-shirt... all she can think about is you or what you both were. She misses you... or should I say has been missing you for a while. She misses all the beautiful memories you both made. Do you remember the day you gave her your T-shirt? Or rather the time she took it to keep warm after you both got drenched in the storm because she's the kinda girl who learnt to dance in the rain.

She misses the way you used to look at her every time she wore something of yours or the time she'd wear that beautiful smile that makes all your troubles go away; in particular the way she made that cute face that highlighted her dimple even more... the one that made you fall head over heels for her. Do you remember the day you both wore blue, both wore your T-shirt's. The day you ate up all her favourite chocolate brownie ice cream while actually you were meant to be feeding her.

She misses the day you had cooked her dinner and were ready and waiting for her when she was back from work; it was perfect, not because you had cooked for her, but because she had had a very long day and even though she didn't have an appetite, she still ate. You know why? Because she loved you and appreciated your efforts that were filled with love and care. Do you remember the day you got mad at her for not answering your calls and coming home a little later than normal? You shouted at her as soon as she walked in without even asking what the matter was. She had gone to get your birthday present engraved. The present that now means the world to you. The engraving on it that brought a tear to your eye at midnight on your birthday.

Did you ever understand her? The girl sitting in your T-shirt right now... missing you... wishing she could talk to you... but she can't because you won't understand... you never did... the respect, care and expressions of unconditional love never were appreciated by you. Do you ever miss her the way she misses you?

The girl sitting in your T-shirt right now, with tears rolling down her cheeks wishing you were there by her side, to wipe away the tears but more than that to take away the pain. The pain she never deserved, the pain she can't handle anymore... the pain that seems to be giving her a slow death. Sitting in your T-shirt... *all she does is miss you.*

"I'm scared"... he said to her.

She was going out of her mind wondering what she had done to deserve this treatment, this sudden disappearance of his, the distance he had formed between them. The cold vibe she was getting from him. Not just for a day or a week, but for almost four weeks; there was nothing. Not a single call or message.

She wasn't one of those clingy, needy or attention-seeking girls so she didn't think much of it for the first few days, as it had happened before, that he had disappeared for a few days. However, he had always come back with some sort of excuse that seemed genuine at the time or rather something she had just chosen to believe him on because that's what you do when you trust someone and deeply care about them.

But did he? Did he care about her the way he said he did? Did he have genuine feelings for her that were actually true? If he did, would he have disappeared like that saying nothing? Not a single word. It is the worse feeling when someone you deeply care about leaves you hanging, leaves you with uncertainty, there's enough in the world without more being added by the ones you love or those that claim to love you.

Coming back almost four weeks later, all she got was 'I miss you too', the message she had sent him a while ago but nothing else. No explanation. No confirmation that he was okay and doing well. There was no reasoning behind his disappearance... nothing at all. And that was frustrating. It meant she didn't know what was going on at all.

Another few days of nothing despite her replying numerous times to the same single message he had sent and then there was the final message that was kind of like the last straw. It said... "I disappeared because I'm scared... scared of how I feel about you. Scared of the strong feelings I've developed for you. And scared of having my heartbroken." And that was all.

She was shocked. She didn't know what to make of it. Yes she was content to know her feelings weren't just stuck in one-way traffic; that he too did feel the same way she did. But then again there is the question of hurting the one you love. If he really missed her the way he says he did would he not check on her to see if she was alright? Would he not message her just to say hi? Life is so, so unpredictable. Anything can happen with the blink of an eye let alone in a month.

If you really had feelings for someone you would never leave them alone. You would want to talk to them all the time. You would want to make sure that you are still a part of their life. This girl had been through a lot of unfortunate incidents recently and he wasn't there when she needed him the most because he was too busy being scared.

He was really scared though. He wasn't your usual guy that falls in love and holds normal relationships. He was more of a Casanova; one night one girl and the next another. But it wasn't his fault; no girl had made him feel the way she did. There was something about her that kept him wanting more. He could talk to her for her hours. Look at her pictures all night and her thoughts would keep him up at night. He was intrigued by her independence. He had never met anyone like her. A girl so independent that she actually made him feel like the needy one in their relationship. She *WANTED* him but didn't *NEED* him. And he had never met a girl who doesn't need a man because he had always met women who needed men for their status, for their money or even for the love that they can give them. But not her she didn't need one. She believed that if she can't love herself; she physically can't allow another to love her. She was so ambitious and determined that her dedication actually inspired him in his work and that is what he loved about her. She wasn't just another girl. Very quickly she had become his inspiration.

That is what scared him. Having feelings for a woman who didn't actually need him. Feeling so strongly for a woman that was like no other. She wasn't impressed by his status nor his money, all she wanted was his time and love. His appreciation for her meant the world to her. But this is what scared because he wasn't used to women like her.

He was scared because he had started falling for her. The girl who was just someone he met casually while having food at McDonalds after a night out. Who knew that the same girl a year later would mean so much to him that he would scared of his own feelings for her.

A Lost Man...

Only when you are lost can you find yourself again...

Six feet tall, dark coloured hair and handsome features made up an investment banker, a man passionate about life, his career, his family, his hobbies and most of all his love. He was a successful and bright man with a lot of potential, enough to take over the world and this is something he knew very well.

The best education, a loving family, a happy childhood, what more could a young boy ever ask for? But he did, he wanted more.

What we see from the outside isn't always true nor is it the real story, hence it is always advisable not to judge a book by its cover. Though it may seem he had a family; a loving family from the exterior but the interior design of his family life was a completely different story. He didn't get along well with his father which is something every son goes through at least once in his youth; many a time due to generational differences, conflict in opinions and in some cases due to the lack of support from the parents side. Not all parents, or rather should I say, hardly any parents understand their children well, their needs, their opinions and most of all their choices. The eldest child of very successful doctor parents does not want to be a doctor and follow in the footsteps of their parents – how is the child meant to explain this to the world when their own parents don't understand it?

Why is it that every choice or life decision a child makes has to get the approval of its parents? Surely there's a reason why God gave each individual human being 'freewill', the ability to make our own decisions and choices in life. Many a time our parents fail to understand that we are our own person too and not just someone they want us to become, we too have wishes and dreams.

He was a bright and ambitious young man; someone who looked up to his father for the man that he was and wanted to follow in his footsteps with regards to gaining success in his career and life. However, his father had other plans. His father didn't support him when he said he wanted to start up his own business, simply because he thought his son was too young and it was a risky move without experience. This caused problems between him and his father.

His gorgeous European girlfriend, who he met while at University, was the reason for another one of his broken relationships. His loving mum who would die for him did not approve of his new girlfriend and that caused a strain on his relationship with her. Finally one day he decided to leave town and start up his business anyway without the blessing from his parents. His business started off really well, surprisingly for a 21-year-old who didn't have a business background, let alone any entrepreneurial knowledge. Guess he just got lucky. However, his luck soon ran out... within a few months actually when his business went bankrupt, his assets lost value and he lost everything and to top it all off his girlfriend of two years left him the minute he lost his business. Safe to say she was only after his money and status.

That day a man broke; into pieces that can't be fixed; he lost everything. The business, his first love and most of all, the trust of his parents. One thing us kids often forget is that not always but sometimes parents do know best. They've got a lifetime of experience and hence, can always catch out the bad ones. Now all he feels is guilt; regret and heart full of pain.

However, everything in life happens for a reason. We may not see it at the time it happens but sooner or later we will always find out. Sometimes things happen in life that break us as a result of which we lose ourselves. But only when you lose yourself can you find yourself again...

The girl on the train

I'd always see her on the same train every single day – the one from Shoreditch and she'd get off at the Canary Wharf station at 8.40am... sharp on time... never a minute earlier or later. Throughout the entire 40-minute journey she'd been sitting in her seat, which was always by the window – always gazing out... as if lost in the view, unaware of everyone around her, the noise of the squeaky train or the annoying passengers in our carriage every single morning.

From afar she was this classy, elegant and well-dressed woman; often in a suit and a serious attitude – you could tell she meant business. It always made me wonder what profession she held... investment banker maybe? But often I couldn't help but wonder what was going through her mind while she stared out the window of the train that we both caught every single weekday morning; what was keeping her so occupied and engrossed that she couldn't acknowledge my existence. I often found myself thinking about her in the mornings on weekends wondering if she was still on the train or what she would be doing at that particular time.

I won't lie I was attracted to her, any sensible man would be; she was drop-dead gorgeous after all and there's nothing more magnetic than a woman that is independent and whose success doesn't depend on a man. Some days she'd have her earphones in, others she'd just sit there like a statue and some I'd see her scribbling down bits of information in her diary. Crossing out dates, writing in little notes and on some pages, she'd just touch the page as if she were trying to feel an emotion; linked with the date on that piece of paper. I once caught her with tears in her eyes; very astutely she looked away towards the window so no one would take notice, but little did she know that I did. For the first time it pained me to see a stranger cry. That day I couldn't concentrate at work at all; I didn't know her at all but it saddened me to see that something could hurt her so deeply on a crowded train so that it had the power to bring tears to her pretty eyes.

I had never noticed until the day that it happened but she had the most beautiful and deepest eyes I had ever seen on any woman; she had long eyelashes and as a guy I only realized this because they quickly covered her tears the other morning – yet another clever trick of hers. The next morning I stared into her eyes; they spoke volumes, you couldn't tell this was the same woman who was wearing tears in them the day before, but there was something about them. It was almost as if her eyes were saying something but only to a certain someone. She had some sort of a blue coloured make-up on her eyelids which went perfectly with her smart formal navy blue dress, but whatever it was, it made her eyes look even bigger and bolder

– as if they were presenting a message that day – one that I failed to read. For the first time after weeks of catching the same train and spending the first 30 minutes of our mornings in each other's company without her knowing, I noticed her curvy figure; as the song goes, she was perfectly shaped like a guitar. Big hips with a tiny waist and perfectly proportioned in each area.

I've lost count of the times I've wanted to speak to her; as cowardly as it may sound whenever she got up from her seat was the exact moment all my courage would disappear on that train. I mean how does a man speak to such a woman that wears power more rightly than any politician, a woman that wears attitude better than the COO of the top 50 Forbes companies, or the woman that wears beauty more purely than a new born baby?

I wasn't sure who or what she was – but what I did know is that I wanted to know. I wanted to speak to this perfectly shaped woman that was everything that I had never experienced in a woman before.

One fine day I decided that I was going to speak to her – it was my birthday and for some reason that gave me courage. I was wearing this navy blue suit with matching cufflinks and had my card nicely placed in my blazer pocket to give her on the train. To my surprise she wasn't there... we would be on the same carriage each morning but she wasn't there. Idiotically I checked the next two carriages in either direction to ours but there was no sign of her.

The girl on the train had gone...

Fools Talk, Cowards Are Silent, Wise Men Listen

Some men are assholes and some men are cowards. What they both have in common is that they both stop talking to you, for no reason other than that they are assholes and cowards. But the worst out of all are the ones that run away from not only their responsibilities but also the promises that they have made to someone they pretended to care about.

I personally cannot even fake a hello let alone a relationship. And then there are those that can fake feelings and even life-long promises. Why is it that men make fake promises and paint a beautiful picture of a future together with a woman they pretend to love with all their heart and soul and then end up cheating on her or abandoning her. How do you love someone but then betray him or her by spending a night with someone else who doesn't even mean anything to you?

It's amazing how people can destroy the one person who loved and supported them at their worst; the one person who believed in them when no one else did and most of all the one person who could have fixed everything? The pain, the mistakes and most of all the will to live; how do you look into the eyes of someone who completely trusts you and accepts you for who you are and lie to them? Lie to their face? How do you hurt someone who did nothing but try to help you?

The difference between a brave man and a coward is; a coward thinks twice before jumping into the cage with a lion, the brave man doesn't know what a lion is; He just thinks he does. There are men that run away from their responsibilities; whether it be a father not owning up to being a father and caring for their child, or a husband not supporting his wife, or whether it be a man who has claimed to love a woman, used her for whatever reason and then left her. But at least there is a reason for why they leave; they don't want to pay for childcare or their wife.

Then there are those that just up and leave, without saying a word, without any reasoning, without any justification. It is almost like one day they woke up and they switched off. Their feelings, promises and commitment of a lifetime all went down the drain.

It amazes me that they don't even think to give you a reason as to why they are leaving. They fail to acknowledge the fact that them abandoning you will break and destroy you. Not once do they think about the fact that every human being needs closure in order to fully move on. However, that is the difference between assholes and cowards; cowards don't think about anyone else but himself or herself and are the most selfish human beings on this planet, most are not even worthy of being called a human being.

Cowards die many times before their deaths;
the valiant never taste of death but once
– William Shakespeare.

CHAPTER 14: A ROLLERCOASTER OF EMOTIONS

Numbness – ever felt numb?

Have you ever felt numb? Do you even know what feeling numb means or what it feels like? The official definition of feeling numb is the loss of feeling all physical sensation. However, it is a lot more than just that. Numbness doesn't just take over your physical sensation; it takes over your mind as well as your life.

Any idea how it feels to not be able to feel anything? Being dazed out when someone is talking to you? Coming across as frozen despite being completely and utterly surrounded by pain. How does one feel nothing when needles left right and centre are poking them? Or when you've been in a life threatening car crash? Or when the one you've loved all your life tells you they don't love you? When your parents aren't there for you when you need them the most? How can one not feel anything? Absolutely nothing? Zilch!

Well one can and you know why? Because that's what happens when you've been broken, when someone close to you has completely destroyed your soul and everything within you, when your trust has been shattered, when you've been abused by the one who claimed to love you to the moon and back and when you've been made to feel lonely by those that had promised to always be there no matter what.

Our body and heart have been broken and destroyed so brutally that it has left them both in such a shock that they can't seem to feel or register any further pain that people or life have thrown at you. Or rather you and your body refuse to deal with it or even come to terms with it. Those unfortunate enough to have been to hell and back at a very young age are mostly the victims of numbness. Life is a journey and a school where all we do is learn, but through classes rather through real experiences. Horrible experiences are enough to break any person let alone when you're young or even in some cases a child. So how do you get over this phase of numbness? Or do we ever? The answer as surprising as it may be is *YES*... why? Because nothing lasts forever, at times we may feel like our life is melancholy but just like happiness doesn't last forever, neither does sadness.

A bitter truth I will enlighten you with is that you're all alone in this world, so only you can get yourself out of this numb state that some selfish, heartless waste of space asshole has put you in. Start by doing things you used to do before you ended up melancholic, bring back the focus on yourself, life isn't meant to be lived on the terms set by other people. You only get one life and you might as well make the most of it.

Truth is we regret more the things that we didn't do than the ones that we did. One day... when you look back from where you are to where you were... you'll realize that nothing lasts forever so whilst the storm lasts... how about we learn to dance in the rain rather than hiding ourselves away in a cave? You never know whilst dancing... the rainbow may appear.

Loss of innocence

What do you think of when someone says innocence or calls someone innocent?

We normally refer to children as innocent or call childhood a time of innocence.

Innocence refers to the time where we are in a state of being acquitted, being unaware of the reality of this cruel world, not seeing the true colours of people; good and bad, not knowing that there's a lot more to people, the world and experiences than just what meets the eye.

It's all well and good when we are innocent, everything seems so black and white, people are either good or bad, we believe that everything will work out just the way we want it to be, that fairy tales are actually true, that Santa actually exists and that one day a Prince Charming will actually come and whisk us away on his gorgeous white horse and take all our troubles away.

But does that actually happen is the real question?

That is called the loss of innocence, actually realizing that all that isn't true, that life doesn't always work out the way we plan it out to be. That not everyone is what they seem to be or what they claim to be. Once we experience this bitter truth in life; it breaks us, shatters the hopes and dreams that we had as a child or up to the time we experienced the loss of innocence, to the time we believed in fairy tales and lived in a bubble.

Whether it's being let down by a parent; the one person we grow up to believe isn't meant to disappoint us, being betrayed by a lover, being cheated on by a person you were dreaming of marrying, being molested by your manager, someone you looked up to as a professional or being left alone in your old age by your only child who you did everything for. Life is full of disappointments and let downs, truths being exposed and turning out to be lies, truths we've believed our whole lives. But the main thing is not letting them break you; which no doubt is very tough to do in most cases because after all we are all only human.

The loss of innocence no doubt does change you, even if it doesn't break you. You'll be a lot more careful with your heart moving on. You won't allow anyone or everyone break you so easily as you did before. You won't give as easily as before because in the past people took so much from you that it left you with nothing. You won't depend on a man/woman to love you or look for their approval your whole life. You'll learn to love yourself, your flaws, your looks, your mistakes because they are what made you who you are today and your achievements; before you let someone else in or let anyone else love you.

The truth is once you've lost your innocence – there's no going back. It's a new *YOU* and there's nothing wrong with the change. So, don't be too hard on yourself, embrace the new *YOU*. Learn from it and move on. Life is way too short to keep looking back in the rear view constantly; after all there's a reason it's smaller than the one in front.

Leaving you...

How do you look at someone and decide it's time to walk away? Holding onto a relationship that you know isn't good for you and is on the verge of dying I won't say it is easy but it's a lot harder to accept those bitter facts and decide that it's actually time to walk away. Walk away from all the heartache, the games and most of all the disrespect.

Love isn't always beautiful, strong, respectful and filled with happiness. Real love involves compromise, arguments and making up, supporting each other when the going gets tough and most of all not giving up at the first hurdle. One of the strongest things you'll ever have to do is at look at someone you truly and deeply love and decide that it's time to walk away – walk away not because you don't love them anymore but walk away because you deserve better and more. You deserve to be appreciated for everything that you do for them and that goes for men and women both. Men need appreciation the same way that women do. There is no gender differences in the way the two species feel when they're not admired by their partner for bringing them flowers for no reason or bringing them a Star Wars Box set when their partner can't stand it. It's the things we do for our partners because we love them or at times simply because we'd know they'd like it. Loving and caring about someone doesn't always have to mean you want something – pure love is selfless.

There comes a time in a relationship where you might not feel that way, where you may not be appreciated, where you may be taken for granted, ridiculed, controlled, verbally abused and the worst one is when the abuse gets physical. A person should leave their partner the minute they experience verbal abuse because if it can get to verbal, trust me physical abuse isn't far behind. Many women think tolerating physical abuse will save their marriage but those dumb bitches couldn't be more wrong. No man should be allowed to raise his hand to a woman let alone his woman, the one he claims to love, the one he vowed to love and protect through sickness and in health. And believe it or not, the same goes for men. Not a lot of men will come out and accept that they have experience domestic abuse by their women only because it may hurt their male ego and reputation of being a real man but either way it isn't acceptable.

And when it gets to that, it's time to walk away because trust me you're not doing either party any favours by staying. Yes you may love them and may want to help them but you tolerating their abuse and disrespect isn't helping them, but is only making you fall in their eyes as well as your own. Having been in an abusive relationship as well as in one where I nor my actions were appreciated I can truly say I wish I had walked away earlier until it got to the point where in one case I was at death's door and in the other I had lost my dignity.

Loving someone doesn't mean giving them the right to treat you whatever way they want, ridiculing you over every petty thing, dictating your life; what you eat, what you wear or whom you might see. Each person has their own life, their own choices to make and should be given the liberty to make their own decisions and mistakes too; that's how we learn, right? Staying and tolerating their behaviour whether extreme or not is easier; you know why? Because you're already comfortable, you're already used to the ill treatment and the abuse.

So why leave? Why leave your safety blanket? Why go from being committed to being single and most importantly being alone? Leaving the one you love is one of the hardest thing you'll ever have to do. The tears won't stop, the heartache – the literal one won't go away that easily, the depression will sink in and you'll miss every damn stupid thing about them. But if you respect yourself enough, you *WILL*. You're not *GOD*, you can't save them. Let them go. There's a reason they say, 'set the one you love free', if they come back they were always yours and if they don't, they never were.

What Doesn't Kill You... Makes You Stronger

"That which does not kill us, makes us stronger". Not many know but this quote is attributed to the German philosopher, Friedrich Nietzsche who said it very eloquently. Studies have shown that trauma survivors regardless of what kind of trauma they have experienced have reported positive changes and enhanced personal development which researchers went onto calling – post traumatic growth.

The truth is there's a reason why this quote so eloquently sums up what we go through post an incident, a trauma or heartbreak. No matter how negative the experience, most people do come out of it the other end. Hence, it is said that what doesn't kill us makes us stronger. Every negative experience we go through; be it mental, physical or the most common killer i.e. psychological, changes us in some way or form. Some experience and accept that change in a positive way and some in a negative way. Where there are some people that accept rejection, heartbreak and bad news and move forward from it by working hard, bettering themselves, there are others that take 10 steps back and give up on life or in some cases take their own life.

Victor Frankl, a neurologist, psychiatrist, holocaust survivor and author of *Man's Search for Meaning*, wrote:

'The way in which a man accepts his fate and the suffering it entails, the way in which he takes up his cross, gives him ample opportunity – even under the most difficult circumstances to add a deeper meaning to his life'.

While some pain and suffering in life are unavoidable and in some way or another part of the human life and experience; it is said that part of it is self-induced by humans as a result of our minds that are taken over by infinite thoughts. Thoughts regarding what has already passed, thoughts of what could have been, thoughts of why something in particular happened, thoughts of why it still hurts, questions of why me? And that is what can drive any human being insane.

However, those who have faith, hold onto that tiny bit of hope and believe that everything happens for a reason and that in the end everything will work out for the best; are always the ones that are okay in the end, they are the ones that experience personal growth and enhancement. Something I have learnt from my experiences, that meant going through hell and back at a very young age is that everything does happen for a reason and also that we might not necessarily be able to see that reason at the time but later on in life we will.

Even in the darkest of times, we see who is there for us and who turns their support away from us. I always believe that is in your toughest of times when you realize who your true friends are, if people you call family are actually worthy of being called that and whether you need to reconsider being there for those who just threw everything you ever did for them back in your face.

What doesn't kill you definitely makes your stronger. It makes you more wary of what is and what should be. It allows you to believe in yourself more, work on your confidence levels more, makes you realize who your true loved ones are and most of all makes you stronger, giving you a kind of strength you never knew you needed.

Whispers – a brutally honest truth

Suicide – an act of a coward as most call it. However, the medical and, I would say, the actual definition is the act or an instance where an individual take's their own life voluntarily out of their own free will. However, if truth be told, every suicide has a hidden murderer behind it, because let's face it no one in their right mind would want to take their own life; unless they were forced to or pushed towards it. It is rather tragic and saddening when such incidents happen. Suicide takes place when someone has been made to feel like they are worth nothing and don't matter at all. It is when they are told, 'no one would care if they were dead' or 'everyone would be better off without them'. This isn't directly taking a knife or a gun and killing someone, but indirect actions in any negative situation are known to do the most damage.

There's a reason why they say words hurt more, after all they can't be taken back. That girl who committed suicide wasn't weak or a coward; in fact she was the youngest ever manager at the country's number one magazine firm, simply because she was good at her work. She died or rather was killed by the local gangster who repeatedly raped her and when the police authorities refused to help her, because the rapist was the son of the local MP, she couldn't live like that anymore. Being raped every single day by the same man who brought a different friend with him each night. That isn't a life. We make a big deal about consent before sexual intercourse takes place. Why don't we make a big deal about rape? A criminal is a criminal no matter whose son he is; right?

That little schoolboy who was only 10 that committed suicide using his grandmother's sleeping pills, did so not because he was ungrateful in any way of the life he had, but because he was scared and in pain. Did you know his so-called religious studies teacher at school was sexually abusing him? And to top it off when he came home to his parents; they refused to believe him deeming him too young to know anything about sexual abuse. They even disregarded the manhandling bruises he had all over his legs. What was he meant to do? What do you do when your own parents don't believe you, the people who brought you into this world?

The young married woman next door that stopped talking to anyone all of a sudden, who wouldn't open the door like she used to before when you wanted to borrow some milk. The disappearance of her make-up and high-end clothes – ever make you wonder why? She was being beat up by her psychopath husband who wasn't even worthy of being called a human being. The beautiful young woman who was once full of life was experiencing verbal and physical abuse. And no, those of you that think physical abuse can't happen after marriage, *IT CAN*. A married woman can still refuse her husband sex if she wants and if he does force her then that is still considered rape. Yes for those of you ignorant species out there a husband too can rape his wife. It all comes down to consent. She took her life because she was sick of being beaten black and blue, day and night along with being raped by a psychopath who was lawfully and unfortunately her husband.

Next time you call someone a coward or call them ungrateful for the life they had that they took, make sure you look up the real definition of what an actual coward is and even glance at the mirror – just to make sure you're not actually looking at one.

You know who are the real cowards? The real cowards are the actual killers behind these suicide;, the teacher who rather than educating children was using them for sex, the husband that emotionally, physically and verbally tortured his wife day and night, the rich gangsters who think they can rape any girl and get away with it, the bullies at school who ridicule other children just to feel superior because they are the ones bullied at one.

Taking your own life doesn't make you a coward, but making someone get to that stage where they are forced into committing suicide is what makes you one. Taking your own life isn't easy – it is not a decision one makes without any thought. It takes a lot of messed up thoughts, whispers of what people will say and have said in the past and most of all the voices that have pushed you to the stage where you are ready to commit the act.

Just like every murder can be prevented so can every suicide, when something seems odd or out of the ordinary, raise your voice, raise a concern. Every human life is precious no matter how old or young. Be there for your loved ones, talk to them when they're quiet, console them when they're crying and question them when they're not being themselves. Be there for them before they're not there to be there for anymore.

Who are Psychopaths?

Another misconception in this world we have is about psychopaths, we consider them to be aliens, killers or those that are outsiders to society; whereas psychologists and scientists who have spent half their lives studying psychopaths and psychology, state that you could have one for a friend, parent, spouse or a colleague. There are a few things we take for granted in relation to social interaction; we think that people see things in exactly the same way that we might do – which isn't true. Everyone has their own point of view and is entitled to their own opinion on matters in life. Psychopaths are people that lack empathy and remorse and hardly feel any emotion. These are the people that in extreme cases won't even care whether you live or dies; some of these are suicide bombers, killers, violent criminals, but by no means all.

You get those that are just plain sadistic, the man that beats his wife every night with a belt before brutally raping her, the boyfriend that physically abuses his girlfriend for every tiny thing that she does that he may not agree with, the psychopath father that beats his wife and kids for no reason, the mother that killed her new born baby child and the list goes on.

These psychopaths act in this way because they have lost all emotion. They don't feel the pain that they are imposing on you, despite being fully aware of their actions. It makes you wonder how and why right? However, it is only because studies show that it is possible to have people who are so emotionally disconnected that they can function as if other human beings are objects that can easily be manipulated and destroyed without any concern or remorse. Due to their psychological problems, at times troubled childhoods and pasts leading to a chemical imbalance in their brains, which can result in their abnormal, animalistic and sadistic behaviour towards those near to them.

But why do we stay? Why do normal, reasonable and logic understanding human beings stay with such psychopaths? Why do they tolerate the abuse, the injustice and at times the repetitive wounds that these psychopaths cause them? In nine out of 10 cases the victim knows the abuser. We stay because we feel we can fix them. The wife who takes the beating because she's too scared to leave in case he harms her kids, the girlfriend who loves the bones of her partner and wants to help him deal with his issues even if it means being raped every night.

But why? Why do we feel like we can't escape? Why do we feel like we need to take psychology into our own hands to help these individuals who are clearly not right in the head. They are different. Not retarded, but definitely in need of help, not ours but serious professional help. Don't categorize a killer as a psychopath because you can't generalise them, psychopaths are all around us – be careful you might be living with one. Don't be scared to leave, it's not your responsibility to change them nor fix them. Leave so that they can get the help they desperately need. Safety comes first.

20 Years Later...

Often people are blinded by the shine of money, power and status, but we all know that only one thing is greater than all of these combined – Love. Love is the only thing that has the ability to make the world go round. This is a story of two people not necessarily in love in an obvious way but a love that they were both unaware of or should I say unwilling to accept.

Young, enthusiastic and passionate about life they both had their own aspirations, dreams and career paths, but the only thing they had in common was their love for each other, which funnily enough they were unaware of. They deeply cared for each other; she was always there for him when things messed up at college and he always consoled her when things went wrong at home with her family. She was there to support him on his first day of university and was also the first one to speak to his girlfriend when he messed up with her despite her own undying love for him. They were the definition of true love, selfless, protective, caring and most of all loving without expecting anything in return. He got jealous of every single male friend she had, especially the ones who were obviously interested in her, despite him being in a relationship with someone else. Such was their love that despite being with other people, they still had feelings for each other that even they were unaware of, feelings that they were not willing to accept. It was unintentional.

One day, long after graduation when they both were in great jobs, she called him and told him that she was getting married. He was happy for her but hearing the news ignited a rather sharp pain in his chest. A pain he had always felt whenever she had been associated with another man. He congratulated her and though he pretended to be happy for her – they both he knew he wasn't, but then again neither was she – not truly.

The day she got married was the last time she saw him. She parted ways with him deliberately because she knew staying in touch would be destructive for both of them. Years passed, they never spoke and then one fine day... bang! They were face to face with each other. She had married a doctor years ago who now wasn't in her life anymore. He had married one of his many girlfriends; a fashion designer. Miss Goody Two Shoes as she had called them – not someone you marry but only someone you can have a good time with. The girl didn't want kids and stayed out late drinking with colleagues and was out of the country most of the time, but mainly she didn't care about him.

They bumped into each other at an Alumni reception at the university he had attended 20 years earlier. She didn't go there but was invited to the reception, as she was now a guest lecturer at the university. Small world, as they call it, the last she had seen on social media he had moved to France so she did not expect him to be there. She had a little boy aged six that she had adopted and he didn't have any kids as he left his wife of five years due to marital problems, so there never was time to have kids.

Twenty years later... there was still that spark between them when they shockingly were brought face to face by fate. Fate that had been written for them the minute they first met 20 years ago at the age of 16. They were always meant to be together but just didn't realize it, nor did they accept it when it stared them in the face. An hour after they had chatted that this was fate bringing them back together they exchanged numbers and decided to stay in touch, but deep down they both knew this was their final chance. Just six months later he proposed and she accepted. They finally accepted fate and had their happy ever after that was always destined for them.

How many chances do you give baby girl ... ?

How many chances are you going to give him girl?

Was it not enough when he screamed at you over nothing?

Was it normal for him to not allow you to wear your favourite dress just because he thought you looked great in it?

Was it not bullying for him to force-feed you despite you saying you had just eaten?

Was it not abnormal for him to order you to sleep when you wanted to sort out your clothes for work before you went to bed?

IF all of this wasn't enough... surely the verbal abuse?

How many chances do you give someone who verbally abuses you?

Do you really believe them when they claimed to love you?
Was the verbal abuse not enough to ring alarm bells?
The same verbal abuse that ended up with you in hospital?
The verbal abuse that caused you to have anxiety and a heart condition?
What were you waiting for? Death? For him to change?
He won't change girl. No one ever does.
Truth is you can't save people with behavioural and psychological problems?
How many chances do you give someone who claims to love you, but yet tries to only control you?
Love doesn't mean control, abuse (verbal and physical), possessiveness, aggression, anger or force.
Love is all about appreciation not ridicule.
Love doesn't involve any kind of abuse. Love is gentle, caring and soft.
How many more chances do you want to give someone who only undermines you in any way he can? And why?
There comes a time when you have to draw a line. Don't give anyone so many chances that they start taking you for granted.

Don't ever give anyone the chance to hurt you twice!

Engourdissement – Numbness

Ever felt nothing? Like nothing at all? No feelings. No tears. No emotions. Simply dead inside. Simply cold. Like a stone.

The feeling of numbness; called engourdissement by the French is a state of being emotionless. A state where you lack all humane feelings that are normal, feeling happy, feeling sad and most of all feeling anything.

What causes numbness?

Feeling numb comes from a long period of feeling way too much. Whether it is too much happiness or too much pain. It comes from having been strong for way too long. Having cried for way too long that you've hit rock bottom.

A state where all your feelings and emotions are just all over the place; a bit too tangled for you to even be able to deal with them.

Feelings are a by-product of our behaviours, so how we think and act has a direct impact on what and how we feel. If we've made a decision that has backfired on us and as result someone we really loved has caused us an immense amount of pain; we might feel guilty and even blame ourselves for the choices that we made. This sense of self-pity and guilt might cause a lack of emotions due to the height of the pain that we might have felt.

At times melancholy results in numbness – having felt an immeasurable amount of pain that has completely taken every ounce of happiness, positivity and willingness to live in you. The rather ironic thing about life is that it is unstoppable... it goes on no matter what. Even death doesn't have the power to put a halt to life. You can become numb and even dead inside but nothing will ever stop, you will still live, you will still go to work each day, you will still do the grocery shopping and eat, you will still meet your friends... life will go on as normal. But the only thing is that you won't feel anything anymore. Nothing at all. Whether that be true happiness, real sadness or the love of an admirer.

Having received the greatest news of your career won't have an impact on your mood or put a smile on your face. Having lost your favourite necklace that had sentimental value won't make you sad. Having someone who loves you make love to you won't feel the same because you'll just lay there like a corpse that is alive. This is what numbness feels like.

Real strength comes from within us

Strength doesn't come from what you can do. It comes from overcoming the things you once thought you couldn't do.

When someone calls you 'the strongest person they know', something inside you breaks a little despite it being a compliment.

Simply because only you and every bone in your body knows how you've managed to stay strong or rather pretend to be strong simply because life didn't give you a choice.

Life can be brutal, full of surprises; often ugly ones. Like when a parent who was your world ups and leaves you when you needed them the most, like when your best friend who was more like a sister to you betrays you because of a manipulative guy, when the love of your life cheats on you, time and time again, pushing you towards another guy who in return chooses to use you as his punching bag and is abusive. These aren't incidents anyone is prepared for. You can't be. How can you prepare yourself for abuse from someone who claims to love you? Be betrayed by someone you trusted with every little secret? Or a parent? Like how?

You don't just become a strong person and neither are you born strong, experiences like these that break you, twist you and most of all teach you about pain are the ones that make you strong because in such cases life doesn't give you any other option. So you've got to buckle up and soldier on. However, not everyone deals with pain like us. Everyone is different, if God made us all the same, life would be pretty boring right? No drama, no competition and oh no comparisons. Though life would be drama free I'm assuming it would be quite dull too.

One thing I think most of us do wrong is that when the going gets tough we turn to our loved ones. I'm not saying there's anything wrong with that but the biggest truth about life is that they won't always be there. Yes they're your loved ones but we often forget that they're human too, they too make mistakes and hence, can't always be there when we need them.

So be your own hero. Trust me you can do it.

Be strong. Be bold. Be beautiful. But most of all just be you.

Don't care about what people will think or say. It won't be for long, people move on from person to person to gossip about quite quickly. This life is about you and you only get one chance, don't lose it or even worse ruin it for the sake of a fake society.

Strength comes from within us.

Surviving...

There's more to life than just surviving... but... sometimes surviving is all you get. How do you deal with surviving? People think you're lucky to survive an accident or an unfortunate incident but are you though? Are you really? What about the post-traumatic stress that you go through? The stress that no one really understands because they're just happy and relieved that you're okay. How do you deal with the scars that the accident has left you with? People look at you in disgust if you have physical scars, but what about your emotional and mental scars, the scars that an unfortunate incident leaves you with.

A car crash that wasn't your fault, a rape by someone who just wanted one thing, a stalker who was mentally unstable, an abusive ex that had psychological issues, a best friend with cancer, or an alcoholic parent – all are incidents that can cause post-traumatic stress. PTSD – Post Traumatic Stress Disorder – A serious condition that can develop after a person has experienced or witnessed a traumatic terrifying event in which serious physical and emotional harm occurred. PTSD is a lasting consequence of severe traumatic ordeals that result in fear, horror or helplessness.

Surviving – for people it doesn't take a lot but for you, it's all you can do. Surviving after a trauma takes it all out of you. It's draining... frustrating even. How do you deal with what has just happened? If you're like me, someone who has seen death so closely, how do you deal with the after effects? You can't help but wonder what if? What if it had killed you? What if you had just gone... just like that? Without having a chance to say goodbye?

Surviving isn't as easy as it may seem, yes you were lucky to survive, be alive, get another chance at life but how do you deal with the fact that you survived? Then there's the fear of it happening again, that abuser striking again or that car hitting you again that caused the worse car crash of your life. How do you deal with that fear? That feeling of it all happening again and perhaps a lot worse this time?

Surviving... there is more to surviving than just surviving.

A beautiful lie and an honest truth

Why is it that most of us are scared of death whereas we all want to live? Life is a beautiful lie whereas death is the most honest of truths.

We think dying means the end of life, but according to me it means the completion of a life. You know when something is completed we celebrate. That is exactly how I feel about death – it brings with it the celebration of life.

Ever thought we all want to live. Life – a beautiful lie; because it doesn't tell us the truth about itself. When we're given a life we're not told about the realities, difficulties and the struggles that we will be facing once we start this journey called life.

When people die, their life ends, their ability to do and say things is taken away from them.

There's nothing else we can do but a lot of people don't realize this. They don't realize that death is such a full stop after which nothing can be written. Not even a comma let alone another word.

Life is a journey; filled with ups and downs, smiles and tears, experiences and opportunities, successes and downfalls. But in the end it's all worth it. The successes bring us happiness and motivation to do more, to do better whereas the downfalls help us see a bit clearer as to where we went wrong and what we could do better in order to improve and actually achieve our end goal.

Life and death are like a pair of shoes, one incomplete without the other. There is no person on this earth who has only experienced one aspect of this duo. Don't be scared of death; as death too is a part of life.

Your Inner Peace

There are too many people out there that have nothing better to do than cause drama and misery. I feel like a lot of people have a lot of free time on their hands; I wish I had that. I personally feel like there are not enough hours in the day for me to get done what I need to do or would like to do.

Once you start working, it feels like that's all you do and having a full-time job tires you out to the point where there's not much else you have energy left for at the end of the day. In a way it's good because having a job keeps you busy and it also means that you are using your brain effectively in a more productive manner unlike some people who use it to cause drama and misunderstandings and then there are some that don't use it at all.

Unnecessary drama, misunderstandings and bullshit just cause a person unnecessary stress and as a result destroys your inner peace. You can try and keep away from it and work towards living a drama-free life, but that is at times impossible because even if you don't cause drama, there will always be someone out there who will involve you in their nonsense.

This is the thing that pisses the hell out of me, when people cause drama for you despite you not having anything to do with the situation. It absolutely baffles me. It can be anything; from your best friend turning against you due to jealousy, from posting something on social media and people coming at you questioning whether it was about them or you not going to a place you used to before. I mean is it not possible that at times you just don't want to go to the same place, is a change of scene not allowed? Can I not change my mind?

I think when a certain post, picture or comment touches the heart of an individual or hits a nerve it is normal to feel something, but I am not one of those childish people to post something on social media about someone who has annoyed me. I believe in actually having a face-to-face conversation with people if they have wronged me and I feel a clarification is needed. But you know what, a lot of people aren't even worth the hassle these days. If people treat you like crap, like a doormat or worse like an option in their life; then you know what, click the goodbye option.

Life's way too short and trust me when I say life's too short; especially to waste it on unnecessary drama, broken relationships and misunderstandings, because guess what, not everything can be fixed and some people are seriously not worth the fight or losing sleep over.

People say you learn with age, but I say that with experience you'll learn not everything is meant to last, not everyone you meet is a friend and not everyone who comes into your life is meant to stay. People come and go, those who matter and are worth the fight will always find a reason to stay; those that don't stay were never meant to and no matter how hard you would have tried to make them stay, it wouldn't have worked.

There are too many selfish and self-centred people in this world who either have nothing better to do in their life than to meddle in yours, or they get a high from causing drama. Whatever the reason maybe, it doesn't change the fact that your inner peace is in your hands. Yes people may pull you into the drama they have worked so hard to cause, but it's your choice to walk away and eliminate any kind of nonsense from your life.

There's good and bad people in this world and in our lives. It's up to us who we want in our lives and who we don't. Never lose your inner peace over anyone because no one is worth losing that over. No one.

Stay strong. Stay beautiful. Stay smiling and most of all stay positive.

Walking away...

Walking away from something or someone that upsets you or keeps hurting you and doesn't make you feel good about yourself is perfectly fine. But don't you think everyone deserves a reason?

For example you wouldn't walk away from a job just because a colleague or your manager has pissed you off over something that is actually unfair. Yes the minority may do that, but the majority don't simply because it doesn't look good on your record as a professional, but most of all as a person. They always say you find out a lot more about a person at the end of a relationship rather than at the beginning. And that can go for any kind of relationship.

Say you didn't have a job for a good six months but then someone believed in you despite your poor interview, not because they were desperate, but because they thought you were worth a chance based on your reasoning and your impressive background. You're happy. You get to pay your bills, save up, sort out your mortgage and once you're financially stable; you up and leave. What? Who does that? And why would you do that to someone? And yes the employer isn't someone you might deeply care about, but always remember if you hurt those that cared about you once... it'll never end well for you. Karma is a bitch.

If we wouldn't ditch a job that made us into a successful professional without a proper goodbye through a resignation, then why do we feel like we can walk away from someone's life that easily? That someone we claimed to love, or in some situations claimed to want to spend the rest of our lives with. Do they not deserve a resignation? Or the least an explanation?

Is giving a reason why they're leaving so difficult? If you find that difficult imagine what it's like to live with no reasons, no answers, no explanation, nothing.

Walking away isn't a negative notion, don't get me wrong but what I do feel is wrong, isn't walking away from a situation without giving a solid reason, leaving it unresolved and running away from it?

Men and women both run away from situations. I myself have done it on a few occasions but one thing I can say that I have never done is walked away from a person without giving them a reason. Because I, out of all people, know how that feels; it breaks you. The human mind is a dangerous place; it can leave you with thoughts you could never have imagined thinking before some selfish coward left you in that situation.

Never hurt anyone intentionally. At times we get so wrapped up in our own lives and self-created messy situations that we forget the unintentional hurt we are causing to those who were always there for us when things were good and held our hands when things were bad. So why is it we forget them when we're trying to fight our demons and inner battles. Isn't that just plain selfish? But hey, everyone's different. Some people are just a lot more aware about the ones around them than just themselves.

People that walk away from your life are the lesson and in some cases a blessing. For example, a husband that was cheating on you behind your back is good riddance, an abusive drug addict partner who is on a road to self-destruction is a blessing to have them walk away from you, because no matter what you would have tried it wouldn't have worked. But those painful departures; your love walking away from you one day without an explanation or a goodbye can kill. You wife walking out on you and your kids one morning when you wake up can be damaging, but like I always say: everything happens for a reason. People also come and go out of your life for a reason. Our life is a movie and people that come and go are just supporting characters. The main cast always stays the same because they're there to stay... always.

Next time you walk away from a tough situation or a person who is no longer required in your life or your movie, don't be a coward. Just tell them. Give in your resignation, then walk away. You'll be able to walk away more freely.

Self–worth

Self-respect, self-worth and self-love, all start with self. Once you stop looking outside of yourself for your value. Why is it that for the first time in my life I questioned my self-worth for you? How could you make me feel so worthless that I lost power to understand what was actually right and what was wrong? Why did you give me love and respect for a minute when you knew you were going to take it all away the next? How could you play with my feelings and emotions like I was one of your PS4 games?

Did you never consider me to be a human being with a heart and soul, unlike yours that is as cold as a stone? Was my worth equivalent to being lied to, cheated and betrayed? Did you even think once before destroying me? The self-absorbed and self-centred creature that you turned out to be makes me question whether you actually even know how many pieces you actually broke me into? For a minute perhaps I had forgotten my self-worth to have actually felt hurt over your actions?

To have questioned my self-worth over your cowardly attitude, to feel like I didn't mean anything only because of your effortless actions towards me? Was I just a pastime, a short-lived entertainment, or a rebound for you? One which you so quickly walked away from?

All those promises and plans to build a life together were a joke? Were they just dialogues as if from a movie that you were rehearsing with me for? The moments we spent together... did they not mean anything to you? You were the first and last person that made me question myself, my self-worth, my being and most of all my capability to be whole... never again. Thank you for making me realize that it was you who needed me, because I never needed you then and don't need you now. I always say that a strong and independent woman doesn't need anyone who doesn't respect or value her. I appreciate your cowardly actions, which opened my eyes to the fact that my value does not decrease based on your inability to see and acknowledge my self-worth.

Where it all becomes too much...

There comes a point in life where it all becomes too much... a time when we're too tired to fight anymore, too broken to keep going any longer and far too shattered to be trying again... over and over again. Life has a funny way of working out... a journey that is filled with twists and turns like a washing machine, ups and downs like a roller coaster and full of unexpected demands and actions just like a toddler. Just when you think you've moved on in life; be it after a break up, a loved one's death, losing a job, a life threatening condition or a near-death experience, it all comes rushing back, the memories, the flashbacks and most of all the tiny details that make it that much more difficult to live and to carry on going.

I mean how do you get past losing the one person that you truly and deeply loved with every breath, bone and beat of your body? How do you get past the fact that the one person who meant everything to you couldn't bear to live their life and so they decided to end it? Under no circumstances is suicide acceptable; especially not when you're escaping life despite having a reason to live it.

They say you're lucky to survive death whether it be beating cancer, beating a gunshot or surviving a dangerous car accident; but are you really though? Is surviving so much better than just leaving without saying a word? Without having to say a painfully goodbye to the ones you love, to the people you may be leaving behind? A cancer survivor might be lucky to beat the life threatening condition but what about the fact that they lost almost everything about them; be it their hair, in some cases breasts, the immense weight loss, but most importantly the fact that they've lost who they were as a person. They might have beaten cancer, but it doesn't mean that they don't live with the fear of 'what if it comes back?'

Someone who has been in a dangerous car accident caused by a speeding idiot that nearly killed them lives with the fear of it happening again, with the flashbacks, the travel anxiety and most importantly the pain of it all. The soft tissue bruising, the ligaments damage and the physical and mental scarring that such traumatic experiences can cause. How do you get past that?

At times people don't understand how you feel because for them as long as you're well and alive, everything is fine; but is it really though? Just because your scars aren't always visible, does it make them literally invisible from your mind and body too?

Why is it that when we have a cold, liver damage, kidney problems or any other organ issue in our body we rush to the doctor, but when there is some chemical imbalance in the brain, going to the psychologist or the psychiatrist is frowned upon? Does that mean we think that our brain is not a part of our body?

The Moving On Circle – a support group for those that have been grief struck; be it a death from suicide, a lost battle with cancer, a road accident death or any other unfortunate end of a life. This is a group of people that get together to talk about different things that such people experience about moving on; talking about the ones that have passed away, the realization about things, acceptance, forgiveness and many other issues that one faces when trying to move on.

But why is it that attending such support groups or meeting a counsellor just to talk to is not seen as normal? Are we insane if we are trying to manage our pain? Or to try to get back to the person we were before we went through something so traumatic that has left us almost numb, broken and detached from the actual world that we live in.

Often everything that we have been through, every single negative experience of our lives can catch up with us and leave us with a grief stricken and melancholic, life, when it all becomes a bit too much to deal with, to juggle and most of all to live with.

"There comes a point where it all becomes too much.
When we get too tired to fight anymore. So we give up.
That's when the real work begins. To find hope where
there seems to be absolutely none at all".
– Cristina Yang

What Drives Jealousy?

An Irish writer named Elizabeth Bowen stated, "Jealousy is no more than feeling alone against smiling enemies," which perfectly sets the scene for anyone reading as to what jealousy is. Most of us, if not all of us, have felt some form of jealousy at one time or another, whether it is a feeling that we experience that we know that we are feeling, or at times one where we aren't aware.

Jealousy is a very natural and instinctive human emotion that everyone goes through at least once in their life, if not more. An emotion where we feel threatened and insecure from someone or something; a particular person or situation or experience that we have had. Most of the time it isn't even the 'smiling enemies' that drive the jealousy but rather the fact that we can see these over-joyful people around us who wear beautiful smiles and appear happy whereas, we are left alone to look like a fool in a corner. Jealousy is derived more from our personal emotions, feelings and circumstances than from those of the ones around us. For example, if someone is feeling quite stressed out at work because they are working really hard but not getting appreciated, they will instantly feel a sense of jealousy if their colleague is more appreciated or in some cases even promoted, whereas they feel almost invisible in such a situation. Another example maybe of two best friends who started college together, but one had to drop out due to experiencing health issues and hence, couldn't complete her education the way her best friend did. There would be a natural feeling of jealousy there because of the other person feeling as though she missed out and is almost envious of the other and perhaps, one would even wish that they had been able to do what the other did or achieve the same.

So it is our own personal circumstances, in some cases failures, decisions and the consequences of our choices that drive the sense of jealousy inside us. This then branches off from emotions of insecurity, feeling inadequate and low in self-esteem. It has nothing to do with another person or someone else's situation.

When we feel unappreciated and not cared for, but see others receiving the treatment we have long longed for, we automatically feel jealous and envious of the one who has received that without even wanting it, or deserving it in some cases. However, what do we know? How do we know what someone else has been through to achieve what they have achieved?

How can you judge the girl with a big diamond ring on her finger standing with her gorgeous husband? For all you know she could have been in an abusive relationship prior to meeting her present husband. What do you know about your new colleague who is so hard working and passionate about work and building their career? To you they might just be a teacher's pet, even though we aren't at school anymore. But have you ever stopped to think that there might be a huge reason for their behaviour, their efforts and most of all their passion? Perhaps they have been through so much in life that work is the only thing keeping them going? Why would you get jealous if they are working hard? Doing overtime? Being appreciated? Like why?

One thing most people often forget is that no one will ever get more that what they are destined for and no one person will get less than what God has written for them. Hence, there is no need for any kind of jealousy, envy and most of all insecurity. When people talk about how they're jealous of me to my face, I can just about hold the tears back and manage the lump in my throat because they have no idea that they have nothing to be jealous of. That nothing that I have achieved has come easy to me, nothing that I have lost hasn't been lost after it had completely broken and destroyed me and that even now I am only here and carrying on with great difficulty. Often people think that letting go is harder than actually moving on, but actually it isn't. Carrying on, not giving up and maintaining an almost non–existent strength is one of the most difficult things one will ever have to do in life.

Jealousy will never get you anywhere in life, in fact it will just destroy what little peace you have within yourself. Rather than looking at others and their life, focus on yourself, look at what you can improve, identify things that you want to do and do them. Nothing that was worth having ever came easy.

Always remember – what is meant for you will always come to you, whether now or later but if it's meant to be it will be yours, but what is not meant for you will never be yours no matter how much you chase it.

Is there a way... any way?

Even years later all it takes is hearing or seeing your name, walking past the place where you first walked into my life, your name flashing on my phone or something I had worn when we were last together... that's all it takes for me to feel that sharp and sudden pain in my chest, for that lump to appear in my throat and for the smile to vanish from my face.

Why is it that you still have that impact on my being, on my heart and my soul?

I mean how can you? It's been so damn long, I don't even remember the last time we both had a decent conversation where you weren't being selfish and I wasn't getting hurt by your words that each hit me like an arrow to a target.

After a very long time this week I felt a pain that wouldn't go away, a pain that left me pale after stealing away my smile, my sparkle and most of all my giggles. A pain that left me with a question that I couldn't find an answer to...'Is there a way?'

Is there a way... any way that we could come together? The question left me doing maths sums on probability and trying to figure out if there was any chance; any chance that I could have you in my life again. That we could start once again... clean slate, fresh start and just us.

I know I walked away but do you blame me? How could I just stand there pretending to be a friend when we both knew that there was always so much more there, the spark, the chemistry and most of all the pure love? Neither of us could deny the mutual understanding and compatibility between us that despite having come across other people, we had never felt with any of them.

I always wondered why our spark never went away, even after so many years... for some reason it still remained. A spark that almost connected our hearts. I never quite understood why you had still maintained it as well. Why was it so difficult for you to let go? Why could you never forget me? Why is it that you could never imagine your life without me as you had said?

How is it that you could say that you never gave us a chance? Why were you always so scared for us? Why were you so hesitant to give me a chance? A chance to make you feel the kind of love that you always longer for and one that I always wanted. Why is it that despite knowing no one else could ever understand you better than I did that you always found a way to escape, to run away from the truth that was between us, the very one that kept us linked to each other for ten long years, the one that never let us stay apart from each other for too long.

A decade that almost seemed like a whole lifetime ago; I still want you. I still want us. The silly girl that unconditionally loves you is still alive inside of me somewhere, who wonders if there is still a chance, if there is still hope for us, for a future where you and I become us? Is there a way? Any way?

The Manipulator Test

If you want an easy way to discern manipulators from empathetic people, pay attention to the way they speak about others in relation to you.

Kind, genuine and decent people will go out of they way to make sure you know their friends and family really like you. Manipulators, on the other hand will always seek to triangulate. They provoke rivalries and jealousy by manufacturing competitions. They whisper in your ear that their friend, an ex or a family member is very jealous of you – or maybe that they said something nasty about you. Make no mistake; they're whispering the exact same things about you to those same people.

So ask yourself; does this person create harmony, or do they solely engineer chaos? Learn the patterns.

For those of you that have met a true manipulator, a narcissist, will know that they are disrespectful, insensitive, inconsiderate, controlling and a bully that uses threats and lies in order to intimidate you. They will disregard your feelings, minimise and trivialise, give you the silent treatment, throw tantrums, the list is never ending. Having been through almost every single one on the list, I can honestly say that I am not at fault, and will also advise anyone reading, don't ever blame yourself for the actions of a manipulator.

They can disguise themselves in the form of a lover, a so-called best friend, a cunning aunt, a spiteful father or any family member. And because all these relations are ones that are so close to one's heart, we are an easy prey for them. I mean, after all, how do you suspect or doubt them when they are someone you blindly trust and deeply love. How would you ever realize until it is too late that the one person you have ever truly and deeply loved is manipulating you into thinking that you are the one in the wrong, that you are the one who is causing the fights in the relationship, that you are the one because of whom your partner is experiencing embarrassment? I mean how does that even work?

From a true story of a young woman who was manipulated by her boyfriend who she had unfortunately fallen for in the worst of times, due to her vulnerability and hadn't known that she was falling prey to a monster who only wanted her to drain the life out of her. The girl who once sparkled like glitter and was as bubbly as champagne was converted into a lifeless corpse, someone who had forgotten how to smile; this was the same girl whose giggles used to echo in the distance of up to a mile. It was only because he was a narcissist who played mind games with her, always made her feel inferior to himself, blamed her for mistakes that weren't even mistakes. He controlled her every move, her every action; what she ate, what time she slept, what she wore, whether she was allowed to go to the gym or not, but most of how and what she was allowed to feel.

This same man who did all the things listed above also claimed to love this young woman who had fallen prey to him. All his actions that almost killed the poor girl were justified by him as a result of his love. What kind of love is that? What kind of love controls another being to the point where they end up in hospital? Where a young girl in her early twenties develops a heart condition? Is that love? Love is calming, peaceful and most of all selfless. It certainly doesn't create fear or anxiety, neither does it kill. Being truly loved can give another being a new life, a breath of fresh air and most of all a reason to live, loving someone to the point where you've pushed them to death's door, suffocated and strangled them isn't called love. It's called controlling, bullying, exploiting and most of all being unable to control your own rage.

What is more interesting is how some of us can actually accept such behaviour and do nothing about it until it is too late? This toleration comes from the way we actually feel about ourselves, from low self-esteem, from low confidence and most of all from feeling a high sense of vulnerability. It is when we are at our lowest, that we are most vulnerable; our shield that we would normally have around us in order to protect ourselves in such times is somewhat invisible or down and hence, we are easy to attack by predators such as these who enter into, not only our lives, but our minds and souls and only leave once they have caused pure destruction.

Always remember: If you have ever experienced a manipulator's poison, don't blame yourself for wanting to taste it; after all, there is a reason God gave us freewill. Some of us end up in such situations solely because we only see the good in people and later on blame ourselves for it. Giving into a narcissist is one huge mistake but don't make a second one by blaming yourself later on. It wasn't your fault.

It's never too late to realize your mistake and move on from the situation. A lesson I learnt at a rather young age was that it is better to eliminate yourself from people and situations that only cause you pain and make your restless. No one in this world, no matter how close to you is worth losing your inner and mental peace.

Limited Dreaming...

There is absolutely no limit to what we can or can't dream about; especially for the dreams that are in our control.

> *'Never let it be said that to dream is a waste of one's time,*
> *for dreams are our realities in waiting In dreams,*
> *we plant the seeds of our future'*
> – Unknown.

Unfortunately, we live in a world where you'll meet more people who will laugh at your dreams than those who will support and encourage you, but that is life. God never said it would be easy, neither did he say it won't be a challenge. To dream means that you are still alive, that you are still hopeful, that you are looking forward, have hopes and plans for the future; and want to live so much more than what you are currently living. You can dream big, you can dream small, dreams can't be measured by their size but more by the happiness and sense of achievement that they bring you.

Getting a job within six months of graduating might not mean a lot to one person but to another that might be a huge dream come true, because for them it means that they can help out their single parent with expenses, or help educate their younger siblings or many other things that perhaps the other person may take for granted, simply because they already have them and haven't had to work hard for them. For a child whose parents aren't that wealth, getting a brand new toy might be a dream come true, whereas for another child that might just be the norm because they always get what they want.

Dreams mean different things to different people and mean a lot more to those that realize that making those dreams come true is a completely different story than to actually just dream about it. Unfortunately, some cultures add a limit to dreams but they couldn't be more wrong because dreams don't have any limits. From dreaming about climbing Mount Everest, to trying skydiving to overcome your fear of heights to doing a PhD alongside having a family life; there isn't anything in the world that you can't do if you put your heart and soul into it.

There are people out there that have come back from death's door, like literally and gone back to achieving things that they always wanted to with or without physical disabilities, there are people who have turned their life around and gotten jobs that they only dreamt of having due to the gap in their resumes, due to the tough situations they were going through, there are people who have lost body parts due to war, accidents or diseases that are still living life to the fullest; from studying a degree, going to work every day to even having a baby.

There is nothing in this world that is impossible; yes certain goals are difficult and can challenge one in a way that they never thought was possible but every obstacle can be overcome as long as one is willing. There's a reason they say where there's a will there's a way.

A little too much, a little too often and a little more each day

How do I tell you just how much I miss you? A little too much, a little too often and a little more each day.

Why is it that it hasn't disappeared? The memory of you, the memory of you and I and most of the lifetime of memories that we created in such a short time.

What felt like a lifetime was only the best six months of our lives. Months in which we lived life to the maximum, as I always used to say; live each day like it's your last because life is way too short to wait until tomorrow.

All the amazing trips we made around the world, the random places we went to and are imprinted forever into our memories, the famous and infamous roads we walked down and at times I danced on. The crazy cuisines we tried, thanks to you being a major foodie, the hip-hop bars we explored, the innumerable pizza nights, walking across the river gazing up at the stars, there is so much we did just in a number of weeks.

How is it that it all happened so quickly? Love; it usually does they say... but only in the movies right? But no, we were a real life example of it happening in real life too. We fell in love with each other the way you fall asleep: slowly, and then all at once.

A love that made us both stronger because we knew we were due to part ways at the end of the six months; we were both very different individuals, we had different career aspirations and did not believe in the institution of marriage, despite the successful married lives of our respective parents that we had both experienced, but there was an underlying fear that we had both been feeling, yet neither of us had acknowledged.

We had engrossed ourselves a bit too much in all the fun we were having, the love that had been blossoming between us, the life that we had both very creatively and beautifully built; a life that only included us, we had isolated ourselves from the outer world because no one else was needed. Our love had occupied all the space we had in each of our lives and hence, there wasn't room for anything or anyone else; or so we had made ourselves believe.

We were not aware of the relationships that we had sacrificed for the sake of ours, the friendships that we were damaging and most of all the destruction we were causing to each other. Co-dependence on another being has never ended well for those that have implemented it in a rather unhealthy manner. There is a reason they say that first one should feel confident and comfortable in your own skin before getting attached to another being. But neither of us were.

Loving each other truly and deeply wasn't meant to lead us to depend on each other for everything, but mostly emotionally that when it came for us to part ways we both bid farewell as two broken individuals who had just lost a huge part, or rather an organ from our bodies and hence, were experiencing difficulty in functioning alone.

How do you expect two people to live separate lives after they've lived like two bodies and one soul for such a long time, how can they function alone when they've become not only each other's love but also a habit. Some people come into your life and take your breath away, other's actually become each breath of yours, without which you don't think you will be able to live.

How do I tell you that I need my breath back? How do I tell you that I need my love back? That I miss you... a little too much, a little too often and a little more every day.

Two years ago...

Two years ago today I felt like my whole life had ended... my soul was crushed into pieces... the strong independent woman inside me was killed.

Someone in whom I had placed my trust for the first time after a rather long time; someone who had promised to protect and love me; someone who wasn't meant to break me, someone who claimed to adore me just the way I was, someone who was meant to be safe and trustworthy, someone... that I thought was saving me.

No one ever expects or is ever ready for the worst that can ever happen; be it an accident, a rape, a sudden death and especially not to experience abuse from a loved one. And that is exactly what happened with me; someone I had trusted and who had claimed to love me had raised their hand to me and placed it rather tightly around my neck leading me to choke and suffocate for a couple of seconds, just enough to have killed me had my neighbour not interrupted the struggle.

How can you claim to love someone and then do that? How do you kill someone you promised to protect and keep close to your heart in a way from where it is rather difficult if not impossible to come back? How does love justify abuse, control and murder?

Death is not the only form of dying; there are so many people that on paper are alive, but if you truly look into their souls, they are more dead than the person that is actually six foot under. Going through abuse can kill a person from the inside; it deeply damages their soul and destroys their being. Have you ever looked at a person and just been able to see nothing? Strange I know. But it happens.

It just takes one incident, one experience of abuse to realise that once your soul has been broken into tiny pieces and your heart killed, your body can still be alive and can carry on as normal. Your body still has the ability to do the things a normal human being does, but just without the actual participation of your soul.

That one incident has killed me in ways I never knew were possible. In a way it all happened so fast, that it feels like it's taking donkeys years to actually process it and accept it all, but on the other hand, at times there are flashbacks that are more like a slow motion movie making me relive each millisecond of it. How do I get past physical abuse? How do you move on from broken trust? How do you let go of what you had thought of as love? And most of all how do you forgive someone who killed you in the name of love?

It's been two years today but I still remember it as if it all just happened yesterday; the struggle, the arguing, the abuse – physical and verbal and in the end that bang. That loud noise of the door, him letting go of my neck and me coming back to life with a lifeline of one last breath. There are times I wake up feeling that hand around my neck, making it difficult to breath as if it isn't already a chore to actually want to.

They say everything happens for a reason, that people come into your life either as a lesson or a blessing and that everything that you go through makes you stronger and makes you a better person in the long run. Here I am just waiting for the long run.

Manhood

Today's 'men' reflect a variety of pictures, ranging from weakness to dimwitted silliness to indifference to feminine sensitivities to carelessness – and beyond. They are given to extremes, lacking control over their emotions and desires. In short, this world produces males who are like puddles of liquid – spineless blobs.

Does anyone know what true masculinity is? Or what it means to be a man?

It seems that masculinity can now only be seen and read about in the history books and musical ballads – perhaps, the only place where words such as 'honour' and 'character' exist.

We live in a world where men are considered as weaklings, where they are cheered on for being in touch with their feminine side, where homosexuality is being promoted more than heterosexuality in men, where men are seen as being trained and taught how to behave and what not to do by the strong and independent women in their lives.

Why is it that men don't act like men anymore or play the masculine role in a woman's life as they used to in the olden days, or as was taught by Adam? Why is it that there is a lack of fathers in the lives of women with children? Why is it that more and more men today are scared to take responsibility for their actions? Is a woman only good enough for a man's ego and pleasure between the sheets at night, but as soon as there is a slight sign of taking a little bit of responsibility or a chance of commitment, they run a mile? Why is it that most men choose to wine and dine a woman and spend as much time with her as possible, but only until they get her into bed?

Why is it that most men are ashamed of being 'whipped' by their women these days? Is it so shameful to be known as being in love with your woman? To be known as a man who would do anything and everything in his power to make his woman happy? Is it so difficult to hold the door open for your woman now?

For today's 'men' is manhood only a display of physical strength in the bedroom behind closed doors or perhaps physical violence in the house? Is that the new definition of manhood for the 21st century man? Is talking to your woman with respect and trying to sort out problems calmly and collectively so unmanly for men in today's society that they must resort to raising their hand?

It is a well known fact that some of the best chef's in the world are men, so why is it that men can't help their wives, mothers, sisters and even girlfriends in the kitchen? Would you look like any less of a man if you were to help out your woman in the kitchen once in a while or even every day? Would it not make you happy cooking for the one you love?

Why is it that chores, professions, certain tasks and certain activities have been divided into male and female? How is it fair that a woman can work a full-time job but then be expected to come home and do housework as well whereas the man is treated like a king only for completing a nine to five job? Only if men knew the amount of work women do. It isn't easy working full-time, doing housework, looking after a child, all while being a woman as well. Only if men knew. If they could be given a chance to be a woman for a day, trust me none of them would last even a few hours. There's a reason God made women a lot stronger than men mentally, emotionally and physically as well; after all no man can go through the pain of childbirth and still carry on like nothing has happened. While men have only been granted with physical strength.

It is extremely disappointing to see that today's men do not know the meaning of manhood but act more like children; where they constantly need a woman's guidance in order to stay on the right path.

If you're born a man, then learn how to be a man as well! Be there for your woman! Don't ever be afraid or shy away from being her man, protecting her and standing by her side each step of the way.

Always remember, manhood isn't something that is proved or shown between the sheets during the night, nor behind closed doors through physical abuse, but something that is displayed in front of the whole world by being right by her side; every step of the way, through every hurdle and every breakdown.

A Special Someone

Now my little special someone might be completely different from what you must be expecting.

My special someone came into my life unexpected and changed my life completely in a way I had never imagined or expected. My special someone isn't an amazing tall, dark and handsome guy that entered my life like a prince on a horse and took all my pain away and we lived happily ever after. My special someone is actually my little kitten Oreo; as the name suggests a black and white little furry bundle of joy, someone that has filled my life with joy and laughter.

On the 23rd of March this year, I was in a terrible car accident where I almost lost my life; I literally, came back from death's door. I often wonder why God cancelled my flight at the last minute, but little did I know how valuably rewarding the compensation would be in the form of Oreo. I have always been a really safe and confident driver, someone who genuinely enjoys driving despite the traffic or the weather. For me to have escaped death in such a horrid way where, after being hit by a car, I was about be crushed by a rather large lorry but luckily or unluckily should I say, God decided to save me, He decided that it wasn't time for me to go just yet.

Nevertheless, the whole accident and the experience of being rushed into hospital and most of all of fearing the unknown was highly traumatic for me. It had a rather adverse affect on me as a human being, I had shut myself down from the world, my body and mind were both in a state of shock; there wasn't much I could say or wanted to do. Driving which was once my favourite pastime had now become the most difficult activity for me.

Then three weeks later, my special someone entered my life, straight away leaving his paw prints on my heart. One of my close friends gave Oreo to me as a surprise present and needless to say it was one of the best ones. Everyone around me had become rather worried and concerned about my wellbeing and I had almost had a character transplant. The giggly, outgoing and lively girl had somehow turned into a corpse that was alive.

Oreo came to me as an eight-week-old kitten and almost straight away became my very own baby; him entering my life almost made me forget or rather stopped me from thinking about the accident and reliving it whenever I was on the road. I had started speaking again, mainly because I had to or maybe wanted to. Looking after him, playing with him and making sure he was alright was had become my sole aim.

I won't lie, it wasn't all hunky-dory as most may think, there were times I'd cry my heart out despite having him, but his cuddles made it just that little bit easier. The car accident nearly killed me; I was lucky to have had no external injuries, but the internal ones are the ones I'm still dealing with almost nine months later. There have been times I have come back from a difficult hospital appointment regarding my damaged back or from having treatment at physiotherapy and I have no idea how, but Oreo has always known and whenever I've come home, greeted him and gone straight to bed to lay down, he has followed me upstairs and with his tiny steps, paw after paw has reached my chest where has placed himself in such a manner as if asking me, 'what's wrong my hooman?' And that alone has been so calming, comforting and soothing in a way. At times like these it is immensely difficult to open up and explain with words how you're feeling and hence, it is a blessing that someone can just understand it all by looking at you, feeling your heartbeat and sensing your mood.

Oreo is a bundle of joy in my life that I could not be more thankful for, someone that has kept me going despite everything that has happened, from the accident to losing someone that was meant to be mine for life. He can sense my mood better than anyone; his cuddles can change my tears to outbursts of laughter as a result of his funny little tactics. He plays fetch like a faithful dog, football like Ronaldo and I call him my baby Ronaldo, and is surprisingly well behaved near the Christmas tree.

Don't ever look for your happiness in another human being; they will always let you down in one way or another. A special someone can come into your life unexpected and in a rather non-human form too.

There are many animals and rescue shelters and way too many kind people that save the lives of those animals when they make them their pet and a part of their family. But for me Oreo came into my life to save me rather than the other way around. Since he was a baby he has always sat above me, whether it be in bed or on the sofa and after a few times it made me wonder why but as time has gone, I have realised that he always did that because he was looking over me as my saviour.

About the Author

There aren't many people out there in this world that have faced the amount and depth of misfortune that Anum Abdullah has and turned it into something positive. She is someone that has taken all the pain and loss that has been thrown at her in life and turned it into her drive, her drive to help others and to make the world a better place.

It is her passion, enthusiasm and willingness to accelerate that has aided her in moving forward from the past in order to create a brighter future.

A people (Human Resources) person by profession, a business woman by intellect, a tutor by choice and just a little bit of sunshine in a world full of darkness by personality. She is someone that can do anything that she puts her mind to... from working on Wall Street, to teaching English to children in China and then to writing in such a manner that her words aren't just read but touch hearts.

Her eloquently pure and raw form of writing touches not only the hearts of those that are close to her but also of those that do not know her and are individuals based in different parts of the world.

There are innumerable situations that we go through in our daily lives that cause us to feel emotions that are often impossible to deal with or explain to another being; these are the experiences that the author has focused on in this book in order to help those that struggle, to inform those that are in denial and to make it just that little bit easier for everyone to deal with all that life throws at them.